M000211048

She Can Laugh: A Complete Guide to Livi
and Physically Well, Copyright © 2016 by Melissa Hughes

The content of this book is for general instruction only. Each person's physical, emotional, and spiritual condition is unique. The instruction in this book is not intended to replace or interrupt the reader's relationship with a physician or other professional. Please consult your doctor for matters pertaining to your specific health and diet.

Contact the author: www.melissaleahughes.com | twitter: @Lissy290 indulgehealthcoaching@gmail.com | instagram: melissaleahughes

Contact the publisher: Unprecedented Press LLC - 495 Sleepy Hollow Ln, Holland, MI 49423 www.unprecedentedpress.com | info@unprecedentedpress.com twitter: @UnprecdntdPress | instagram: unprecedentedpress

Scripture quotations marked (NIV) are taken from the Holy Bible, New International Version®, NIV®. Copyright © 1973, 1978, 1984, 2011 by Biblica, Inc.™ Used by permission of Zondervan. All rights reserved worldwide. www.zondervan.com The "NIV" and "New International Version" are trademarks registered in the United States Patent and Trademark Office by Biblica, Inc.™

Scripture quotations marked (AMP) are taken from the Amplified Bible, Copyright © 1954, 1958, 1962, 1964, 1965, 1987 by The Lockman Foundation. Used by permission.

Scripture quotations marked (ESV) are from the ESV® Bible (The Holy Bible, English Standard Version®), copyright © 2001 by Crossway, a publishing ministry of Good News Publishers. Used by permission. All rights reserved.

Scripture quotations marked (NLT) are taken from the Holy Bible, New Living Translation, copyright ©1996, 2004, 2007, 2013, 2015 by Tyndale House Foundation. Used by permission of Tyndale House Publishers, Inc., Carol Stream, Illinois 60188. All rights reserved.

ISBN-10: 0-9861931-4-3
ISBN-13: 978-0-9861931-4-9

Printed in the United States of America
Ingram Printing & Distribution, 2016
Lifestyle photos by Olivia Ezinga

First Edition

Unprecedented Press

she can laugh

A guide to living
spiritually, emotionally
& physically healthy

MELISSA LEA HUGHES

DEDICATION

I'd like to dedicate this book to my incredible husband, soul mate, and hero Keane Hughes. No one has taught me more about how to have fun, believe God for big things, and live fearless like you have. I owe many of these revelations to you! I love you pumpkin.

ACKNOWLEDGEMENTS

I want to give a special thanks to Josh and April Best for editing, designing and publishing this book for me. I don't know how I could have done it without you two! Additional thanks to Rose White for proofreading and Olivia Ezinga for her photos.

I also want to thank my mom for always being there for me, seeing the best in me, and encouraging me to pursue my dreams. I love you!

Finally, I want to thank my in-laws and church leaders, Andrew and Angela Hughes. You have poured so much into my life. I have learned so much from your lives, and I'm eternally grateful. I love you both!

*"She is clothed with strength and dignity;
she can laugh at the days to come."* (Proverbs 31:25, NIV)

INTRODUCTION

Health is more than what you eat and doing crunches. We are a spirit that has a soul and lives in a body. We are first spirit-beings. Rarely, if ever, do people contemplate their spiritual or emotional fitness. I would know because I used to be one of those people. It wasn't until a few years ago that I began to understand health as holistic. If we are going to have a mind, body, and spirit health transformation, we must look at all aspects of our lives.

As a certified holistic health coach, I have found that many women's health issues are not due to a lack of self-control and discipline (although those things do play a role), but rather due to an imbalance in a different area of life. The food is not the root issue but only a symptom of a deeper craving. Many times we look to food for comfort, love, fun, excitement, or entertainment instead of finding those things in God. Have you ever eaten a whole pizza or a bit too much ice cream because of a devastating life event? Have you ever struggled emotionally with a certain circumstance before getting God's perspective? Then, due to your emotional low, you've eaten an order of extra large fries or too many twinkies because it's been a rough day and "you deserve it." At least, that's what we tell ourselves.

Here are 7 ingredients of a healthy lifestyle:

1. *Authentic Loving Relationship with God & Yourself*

2. *A Sense of Purpose Through the Pursuit of your Calling*

3. *Rest & Self Care*

4. *Responsibility for Emotions & Condition of Your Heart*

5. *A Positive Community and Relationships*

6. *A Regular Exercise Routine*

7. *Healthy Food*

In my experience as a holistic health coach, these are the most important ingredients in maintaining a happy and healthy life, and I've based my book off all seven. I pray that you find each chapter challenging, encouraging, and motivating.

Health is more of a discovery about yourself than anything else. It's important to enjoy the journey on the path to a healthier you instead of beating yourself up for a number you see on the scale. You're so much more than a number; you're a child of God!

Love,
Melissa

CHAPTER 1

ferocious babes

I am the type of person that has a long track record of blurting out the first thing that comes to my mind the moment I think it. A few years ago, I was at the store and found myself chatting to one gentleman and an older looking woman. When I introduced myself to them, I accidently mistook the man's wife for his mother. They were husband and wife, not mother and son!

As I was driving home from the shop, I kept replaying the scene over in my head and feeling so embarrassed. I got lost in the memory as I lingered on the whole situation. I began to beat myself up for completely misreading the situation.

In the midst of this conversation I was having with myself, I suddenly heard God gently say to me, "Melissa, you are my Ferocious Babe."

I heard it so loud and clear that I was shocked. I obviously wasn't in an attitude of prayer. I had no worship music playing in my car, and it just came out of nowhere abruptly interrupting my stream of thoughts.

Thinking about it, I realized in the midst of my subconscious self-loathing, God was taking absolute delight in me! I repeated that nickname aloud to myself in the car, "Ferocious Babe," and as I continued to think it over, I completely forgot about the embarrassing situation that had just taken place. My spirit lifted inside me. He called me his Ferocious Babe.

Truth be told, I never thought that God, the Almighty One, the Lord of Lords, the Holy One, the God of the Universe (are you catching the reverence here?) would stoop down and say something so intimate and so personal to me. In my head, I knew God loved me (of course, he has to right? He's my Heavenly Father), but I didn't realize he actually liked me.

It was strange to comprehend that this perfect God took amusement in my not-so-perfect every day life. While normally, I would have classified that embarrassing moment as an opportunity to better myself, he clearly paid no attention to any of that religious stuff. He was focused on something else.

Me. Just me. And he seemed happy enough with just that.

To me, the nickname carried with it a certain message. While I would have thought I was a bit clumsy and awkward at times, it seemed his thoughts towards me were something more along the lines of: cute, beautiful, fearless, and courageous.

To myself I was one thing, but to God, I was his Ferocious Babe.

UNIQUELY LIKED BY GOD

Song of Solomon is a book full of God speaking intimately and lovingly to his people.

"But my dove, my perfect one, is unique...The young women saw her and called her blessed; the queens and concubines praised her." (Song of Solomon 6:9, NIV)

You and I are uniquely liked by God. That day, I realized while many of us can spend so much of our time trying to be something for God or trying to attain a certain standard of godliness for him, he sits there with his eyes fixated on us already charmed with us.

As women, we need to know that we know that we know that we are God's Ferocious Babes: his little girls, his daughters who are totally loved, totally accepted, totally forgiven, and totally beautiful. We are enough and never too much, hand-picked, and never forgotten. We are totally secure and never left behind. We are his beloved. The sooner we grasp that truth, the sooner we can receive the love he has already poured out on us.

THE MARY AND MARTHA CONUNDRUM

One of my favorite stories in the Bible is the story of two sisters, Martha and Mary.

"As Jesus and his disciples were on their way, he came to a village where a woman named Martha opened her home to him. She had a sister called Mary, who sat at the Lord's feet listening to what he said. But Martha was distracted by all the preparations that had to be made. She came to him and asked, "Lord, don't you care that my sister has left me to do the work by myself? Tell her to help me!"

"Martha, Martha," the Lord answered, "you are worried and upset about many things, but few things are needed—or indeed only one. Mary has chosen what is better, and it will not be taken away from her." (Luke 10:38-42, NIV)

As women, we can be distracted by so many things all the time. It can be our own short-comings, our children, our housework, or our career. We always seem to be busy, busy, busy. In this story, Mary chose to sit at Jesus's feet and listen to him, while Martha stood there frustrated because Mary wasn't helping her.

Instead of Jesus siding with Martha and telling Mary to get her butt up and help, he says, "Mary has chosen what is better." Most of us would have initially thought that getting the house ready for the Son of God would have been much more of a priority, but Jesus saw it was more important for Mary to sit and be with him than finish preparing.

First and foremost, God wants a personal and intimate relationship with us. He isn't interested in what we can do for him, how hard-working we are, or how gifted or talented we are – he is simply interested in us. Just because it's us! Unfortunately, Martha was so concerned with making sure the house was in order that she completely lost sight of what the purpose was in having Jesus there: to spend time with him and get to know him. When we sit with Jesus, listen to him, and worship him, we actually begin to understand how he sees us, how much he loves us, how captivated he is with us, how much he cares for us, and how interested he is in us. We can't enjoy our relationship with him when we pull a Martha and think we need to have it all together before we come to him. The truth is, we will never have it all together enough in order to come to Jesus. In fact, he died for us so we didn't have to be perfect for him. He became perfection for us. His whole goal with us is simply togetherness.

The more I walk with God and am part of a church, I realize how so many of us struggle with the fact that God not only loves us, but he actually likes us. It is so easy to see the worst in ourselves. We struggle to accept the fact that God always sees the best. We can't accept that even when we absolutely blow it, he still hasn't changed his mind about us. That, when we remain faithless, he remains faithful (2 Timothy 2:13). His love for us is bigger than we think.

Around the time that God began to speak to me about

being his Ferocious Babe, I really struggled to believe it. I knew that God loved me, but when I actually took an honest look at how I felt about myself, I realized I knew his love only on a theoretical level--not an intimate one. I only seemed to know God's love when I thought I deserved it. I didn't know that God loved me even when nothing I did warranted his affection.

GIVE YOURSELF PERMISSION TO BE LOVED

Romans 12:2 says, "Do not be conformed to the pattern of this world, but be transformed by the renewing of your mind." (NIV) It's easy to read this scripture, highlight it, underline it, and put a nice note next to it, but when it comes to actually changing the way you think about something (especially yourself) it isn't easy. In fact, it takes humility to honor where you are and receive his love exactly where you're at in this moment to help you move forward. It's when we stay in a place of jealousy or envy of other people that we remain stuck in our own issues.

I began to remind myself every single day that I was God's Ferocious Babe and that he loved me exactly how I was. Every time I would make a mistake, feel stupid, or feel insecure, I would choose to boast in God's love for me. As much as I naturally defaulted to old ways of thinking by beating myself up for whatever I felt wasn't "good enough," I would remind myself aloud that I was God's Ferocious Babe. Those times were the most difficult but most crucial moments to keep his thoughts about me above my own. The more I began to do that, the more I began to believe it.

It certainly was not an overnight process, and even as I write this book, I'm continually growing in that revelation. But this was where I began to enjoy myself and my relationship with God. I found myself more comfortable in my skin; I didn't feel the need to prove myself to God or anyone else. I was happy just being me because I started to receive a greater measure of his love for my life. I was finally allowing him to love me.

One time at church, I saw a dad holding his two year-old daughter in front of me. The girl must have decided she was done being held because she began to kick and whine. The dad continued to hold her tighter and stroke her blond, curly hair, quietly saying, "Shhh, it's okay! It's okay!" But she started to make an even bigger fuss, and eventually he just had to put her down. The Lord spoke to me and said, "I can only love you if you let me." I know that God loves us regardless of whether we want it or not, but the ability to receive his love is another story altogether.

I found there were so many times where I was so frustrated with myself, with life, with whatever, that I would "kick and whine" about it to the point where God just let me do it. He allowed me to have a pity party for myself, as long as I allowed myself to do it. For some reason, it's natural for us to want to hide from God when we make a mistake instead of run to him. We want to try to solve the problem on our own. It's an independent spirit. We are called, though, to live dependently on God. The trick is to run to him and not run away from him because it's his love that will calm us down, comfort us, and soothe us if we allow him to come close in our time of need.

We must learn to be like Mary and live a lifestyle of "sitting" with him and allowing him to pour out his love on us every single day. We can't be satisfied with a theoretical knowledge of his love or even last year's revelation of his love for us , we need to know it every day. It's one of the healthiest things we can do for ourselves.

That might not look like taking an hour out of your day each morning, and having everything completely quiet and peaceful to sit with him. Although, we should make a regular habit of doing our best to create space in our lives to do that. Many times though, this can happen when dropping a kid off for one sport and taking the other kid to the next. We can say to God, "I know you love me. I'm so thankful for your love for me today. I need it, and I thank you for it Jesus. Amen." It's simply staying connected to him in whatever way that looks like for you. It's being mindful of his loving presence throughout the day. There is no set formula for any one person; that's the beauty of it. It's your own personal relationship.

MAKE ROOM FOR HIS BIG LOVE

I absolutely love Ephesians 3:18 when Paul prays for us, "to grasp how wide and long and high and deep is the love of Christ." (NIV) If we are going to actually grasp that big love, we need to start to make room for it in our hearts.

We can't be full of self-hatred, self-condemnation, or personal regrets. If we are, then we can only make room for a little bit of God's love for us. When we open our hearts up to God and begin to believe the love he has for us remains, all that other junk will fall away regardless of our own opinions of ourselves, our past, or what others have said.

The goal is to be captivated by the kindness, the compassion, and the mercy that God has for us no matter what we have or haven't done. It's absolutely liberating! He never looks at us with eyes of condemnation or disappointment but with eyes of compassion and grace. When we stare into those eyes, we become empowered by his love, and we are transformed from the inside out.

Some people believe the "grace message" only encourages people to continue to sin. Every time I've turned to God and looked into his eyes of love and grace toward my life, it never gives me a license to continue sinning. Instead, it only inspires me to live like Jesus lived. We cannot be afraid to open ourselves up to God completely and allow him to love every part of us; not just the pretty parts but also the not so pretty parts too (in fact, those are the ones that need the most love!). It is imperative for us to hold onto and revel in his love – to snuggle up close to him. It keeps us motivated, healthy, inspired, and empowered to live this life!

The fact that God never forgets to call the sun up every morning is a reminder to all of us that he is a faithful lover to every person on the planet regardless of where we come from.

HE SEES WHO WE ARE CALLED TO BE

In the story of Gideon, God speaks to him in Judges 6:12 and says, "When the angel of the Lord appeared to Gideon, he said, 'The Lord is with you, mighty warrior.'" (NIV) In verse fifteen, Gideon says, "But Lord how can I save Israel? My clan is the weakest in Manasseh, and I am the least in my family." (NIV) You see, God saw Gideon as a mighty warrior, but Gideon saw himself as the weakest in his family.

Have you ever felt like the weakest in your family when God is saying you are his Ferocious Babe? The thing I love about this nickname is the fact he said I was ferocious when I felt like a little church mouse. He was clever by using the word *ferocious* because as women, we aren't called to be quiet, timid little church mice that get the scraps of whatever is leftover. God has called us to be fighters, women of faith, women who are fearless and determined, women who aren't shy or bashful about who they are, women who choose to be strong in God and put their trust in him, and women who are confident in the love their heavenly Father has for them. Let's bask in God's love for us everyday and live like the strong and beautiful women we are. We are his Ferocious Babes.

APPLICATION POINT:

Take some time to pray and ask your heavenly Father how he sees you. When we align ourselves with his thoughts for who we are, we begin to see ourselves correctly. Whether he gives you a nickname, a picture or a phrase, ask God to show you who you are to him.

Apple Nut + Plum Quinoa Porridge

INGREDIENTS:

1/3 cup quinoa

1-2 Tbsp peanut butter

1 frozen banana

1 ripe plum

1 apple

1 small handful of chopped almonds

sprinkle of cinnamon

DIRECTIONS:

Boil 2/3 c water in a pot. Add the quinoa and frozen banana, and put the cooker setting on simmer. Occasionally stir the quinoa and the banana until everything becomes absorbed with the water and banana. Add in the peanut butter and stir. Transfer the mixture into a bowl, add the plum, apple, almonds, and sprinkle cinnamon on top. Enjoy!

Peanut Butter + Jelly Smoothie

INGREDIENTS:

1 handful of kale

5 black berries

1 plum

1/2 c brown rice milk (or nut milk)

1 frozen banana

1 Tbsp organic peanut butter

DIRECTIONS:

Blend and enjoy!

CHAPTER 2

electric blue

Recently, a friend of mine went up for prayer after a women's conference held at our church. She was in a spot in her life where she was working a job that was stagnant, comfortable, and lifeless. But she was very good at it. She knew it backwards and forwards, she was praised by her manager for her excellent work, she received great vacation and benefits, and she lived very comfortably; however, there was no passion. No life. No real meaning.

Sound familiar?

When she went up for prayer, she was encouraged

with a picture that God gave the woman praying for her. She said to her, "I see you at the store in the nail polish section looking at the polish colors. I see you choosing your usual colors like the pinks, beiges, and reds. God wants you to stop with those boring colors and wear something new, something different, something risky, something like...Electric Blue! And while that may not be a color you would choose for yourself, God wants you to realize your future, to get outside your comfort zone, to take a risk, and to wear Electric Blue because that is where you will find blessing."

This picture was exactly what she needed to hear. It hit her right between the eyes, and God couldn't have been more clear. He showed her that she was comfortable in her cushy 9-5 job with great pay, benefits, and vacation time. While it looks secure and peaceful, it was actually killing her on the inside. In fact, the best place for her to be was outside her comfort zone in a place of risk and in a place of faith. It was actually the most secure spot she could ever be: in a place where she was willing to put her future in God's hands instead of the state of the economy, small thinking, fears, and comforts.

The more I think about this encouragement to my friend, the more I believe she is not the only one in this situation.

ELECTRIC BLUE VS. BEIGE

You are electric blue. Too many of us think of ourselves as beige. We don't think we have very much to offer with what God has put in our hearts to do. We downplay it. We make it small. We dilute its vibrant color and call it beige. We see other people and think they would be better suited for the job, but when it comes to ourselves, we struggle to see our potential. I dare to tell you, you are not beige by any stretch of the imagination; you are electric blue!

None of us are called to live boring lives in God. None of us are called to simply survive. Similar to my friend, when we choose a lifestyle based on its comfort and security, it can sometimes be a graveyard for the prosperity of our souls. While that road does offer ease and predictability (which does seem nice), it's usually just short of the electric blue adventure God is always trying to call us to live. While living electric blue doesn't always offer the same security and comfort, it normally brings about deep fulfillment and satisfaction within ourselves.

We were created to take action, pursue our God-given mission on the planet, and do it with gusto – no matter what it might be. In order to live with a true sense of purpose, meaning and fulfillment, we have to live an electric blue lifestyle. I've learned that the Holy Spirit likes to keep us on our toes in three specific ways; The Big and Dramatic, The Boring and Mundane, and in The Dirty Work.

THE BIG AND DRAMATIC

One of my (and my mom's) biggest aspirations for my life was to get a college degree (something she had always regretted not getting herself). After years of hard work, lots of studying and exams, I was accepted into my top choice school with scholarships.

As my time in college progressed, I had gotten a fantastic job, I was very involved on my campus, and I had great grades and lots of friends. I was on the road to success. Shortly into the first week of my second year of college, the Holy Spirit came to me and challenged me in The Big and Dramatic.

At the time, I was not walking with God in a personal way, however, a friend had invited me to go to church with her one Sunday. While there, someone mentioned to me a program being offered where young adults take a year out of their lives to serve in the church and grow in their relationship with God. The program started in three days. When I left church that day, something inside of me was urging me to do it.

In all honesty, my mind couldn't comprehend why God would call me out of something so wonderful. Why he'd ask me to leave my college education, give up all my scholarships that I worked so hard for, disregard my mom's best wishes and leave my amazing job. Everything was going as planned, why would he want me to give all that up?

Three days later, after much contemplation and sifting through different outcomes with immense external pressure from teachers, family members, and friends, I dropped out of college to pursue this calling God had suddenly put on my heart. It was the most petrifying, scary, and sleepless three days of my life! To all of my friends and family members, it was the most irrational, unwise, and risky decision I could have made. But it was God.

To say it was safe, convenient or easy would be a lie. It was everything but those things. I had never felt more uncomfortable in my entire life. At the same time, it was one of the best decisions I ever made. From that day, God launched me into my destiny. I came into a deeper relationship with Him, family members received salvation, I met my husband at that church, and I discovered a greater purpose for my life than I could have ever dreamed up on my own. I became Electric Blue.

And in case any of you were wondering, I did end up going back to school and finishing my degree. Turns out, God is also interested in sticking to our commitments, more on that later. For now, though, I like to call those Holy Spirit moments, The Big and Dramatic.

The Big and Dramatic is when God opens a door for us in a moment in time, and if we don't jump through it, we miss out on something wonderful in our destiny with him. The Greek word kairos perfectly describes this type of moment in time. Kairos moments are rare, but when they come, they accelerate us into something amazing in God. But, they usually require guts – lots of guts!

Unfortunately, these moments have been missed by many due to comfort, fear, people pleasing, worldly wisdom, and a lack of trust in the goodness of God. Take a look at this story from the Bible where a rich man misses out on a date with destiny due to being comfortable and fearful.

A rich man approaches Jesus and asks him about eternal life. When the young rich man tells Jesus everything he has done to earn eternal life, he asks Jesus what is he still lacking:

Jesus answered, "If you want to be perfect, go, sell your possessions and give to the poor, and you will have treasure in heaven. Then come, follow me." When the young man heard this, he went away sad, because he had great wealth.

Then Jesus said to his disciples, "Truly I tell you, it is hard for someone who is rich to enter the kingdom of heaven. Again I tell you, it is easier for a camel to go through the eye of a needle than for someone who is rich to enter the kingdom of God."
(Matthew 19:21-24, NIV)

This is a clear picture of when God comes to you in The Big and Dramatic. The rich man was clearly very successful. He had everything in the natural but inside, there was a lack of satisfaction in his heart because he was longing for eternal life. When Jesus responds to him and tells him that he must sell everything and give it to the poor, it wasn't because Jesus didn't want him to have material possessions. He was offering him an exchange:

his lifeless lifestyle of comfort, security, and wealth for an electric blue adventure of faith in God. But he had to make a decision in that moment.

Scripture tells us that the man went away sad. I can imagine this rich man weighing all this up in his heart, feeling an immense pressure from fear of potentially not being able to provide for his family if he sold all he had, having doubts of what it might do to his reputation, and the inconvenience it would be to loose all that wealth. Unfortunately for him, what Jesus was asking him to do was too uncomfortable. He lacked trust in God and forfeited his eternal destiny because he didn't want to take the risk.

I wonder if the people standing by that day thought that man made a sensible, responsible, and wise decision. The thing is, when the Holy Spirit offers us these kairos moments in time, they rarely seem wise to outsiders. But to the spiritually minded, they can recognize it as a God opportunity.

The question I'm posing to you is this: are you willing to compromise what God has for your life to remain in a place of security, comfort, and fear? If the Holy Spirit comes to you in The Big and Dramatic, it is paramount for not only the health of your soul but also for the eternal purposes of God for your life, that you jump through that door. Life is too short to wonder "what if" for the rest of your life. Regret is a terrible disease for your soul. If you want to stay satisfied and full of a vibrant life in God, tell your convenient, safe, and predictable lifestyle to take a backseat.

Although The Big and Dramatic might come around once in a blue moon, the Holy Spirit loves to offer us an electric blue lifestyle in, believe it or not, The Boring and Mundane.

THE BORING AND MUNDANE

The Boring and Mundane means the Holy Spirit will offer us opportunities to step out in some way or another in our everyday life. Perhaps it's not God challenging you to do something as wild as leaving your job, but he is challenging you to live electric blue by adjusting an attitude you have, tweaking a mindset you're in, letting go of a bad habit, or tightening up the way you conduct yourself in some manner.

I can remember a time when God was teaching me about the importance of doing what I said I was going to do. I was the sort of person who you would meet initially and flittingly say something like, "Hey, it was great to meet you, let's get a coffee sometime!" Then, I would never follow up with that person. God began to reveal to me that my character needed adjusting because if I was going to be the person he was calling me to be, I needed to be a person of my word. While it's not big, glamorous, or exciting, God often tests the obedience of our hearts in the details of our character and everyday lives.

I must admit, it wasn't easy or comfortable to make the shift because I wasn't used to being a person of my word. However, I knew I needed to make the effort and change so I could position myself for more of whatever God was calling me into.

God is into your character, your daily choices, your everyday life. Living electric blue looks like being obedient to whatever the Holy Spirit is asking you to do. Following Jesus is not a one time decision, it's an everyday choice. Sometimes the big life decisions are more obvious, and we can seem to pay more attention to them because it's such a large life change. Unfortunately, many times, we can ignore the small steps of living our lives radically for God because we don't think it really matters. However, God is interested in the details of who we are and what we do. In fact, it's those daily decisions that sometimes lead us into our big and dramatic destiny.

Perhaps God has been asking you to begin changing your diet, join a committee at your child's school, sing at church, start a blog, be more vocal about your faith at work, or go back to school. God is into the everyday, menial ways we can live our lives out-loud for him. In fact, God takes great delight in the Boring and Mundane decisions we make to be obedient to his voice.

In 1 Samuel 16, when God was looking to appoint a new

king over Israel, he tells Samuel to anoint David, the shepherd boy, as the new king out of all of his seemingly better candidate brothers. David was led into his destiny with God by being faithful in looking after the sheep; how very boring and mundane. We cannot discount these small promptings of the Holy Spirit to step out in our daily lives because it is the little things that can matter the most to God.

Whatever it might be that God is challenging you to step into, it's so important you tell your fears or sheer laziness to take the backseat. Because when you pursue God's purpose for your life, it always brings blessing.

THE DIRTY WORK

The last way the Holy Spirit challenges us to live electric blue for God is in The Dirty Work. The Dirty Work is the time in life where we wish we could just quit school, quit our job, or stop being faithful in the boring and mundane. But the electric blue thing to do is to be patient, to endure the season, and not quit. I sometimes find these are the most difficult times to live electric blue for God because it requires endurance and patience.

I will never forget a time when a friend asked me to go for a run with her. Because I am into healthy living, people sometimes assume I enjoy all exercise, but I don't. I am not a runner. I am slow. I cannot run very far, and I run like a fairy because of my dance background. But, I did want to spend time with my friend, so I agreed to go for a run with her.

I expected to run for a maximum of two miles, and I would have been proud of myself for that. However, after about two and a half miles, we were still running. At that point, I was done. I felt like I had hit my max. Barely being able to get the words out of my mouth, I told my friend that I had to stop because I couldn't go any further. She said to me, "We're nearly there! Just keep going!"

Due to my trusting nature, I believed her and continued running. Big mistake. After another three minutes and not seeing any end in sight, I told her again that I was done and I needed to stop. She reassured me again saying, "We're nearly there! Keep going!"

This must have happened at least five or six more times, and by the time we finished, we ran five miles! To some of you, that might be a piece of cake. I had never run five miles before in my life. I couldn't believe I actually ran that far. My face was red and my body was sore for a week, but I went further than I ever had thought I could.

Sometimes our lives are like that with God. He will have us do something and in the beginning it's okay. But there comes a point where we want to just quit and we feel we've had enough. Just as we feel we are about to throw in the towel, the Holy Spirit whispers to us, "You're nearly there, just keep going!" Sometimes we don't know how long the season will last. We can't see an end in sight, and all we want to do is stop. However, continuing to stay faithful until the end in whatever God is telling us to do, regardless of our feelings is an electric blue quality.

Many times we find we are a lot stronger than we think

and when God stretches us, we grow into another dimension of who he is calling us to be.

The point is, we should stay obedient to whatever the Holy Spirit is saying.

We must choose to be more concerned with stewarding the callings, giftings, and talents God has given us rather than our own comfortable lives.

WE MUST CONFORM TO GOD'S STYLE, NOT OUR OWN

We all must make the decision to give ourselves to God 100%. Even though it's not always easy, sensible, convenient, or safe. I've found that most of the time that is God's style. He's totally sovereign. God does what he wants, when he wants, and how he wants. It's up to us to surrender to him – not to the pattern of this world.

"Do not conform to the pattern of this world, but be transformed by the renewing of your mind. Then you will be able to test and

approve what God's will is—his good, pleasing and perfect will."
(Romans 12:2, NIV)

What good is it to conform and believe you're beige when God is calling you to stand out and be electric blue? When you live vibrant and pursue the thing God is calling you to do, you are able to test and approve what his good, pleasing, and perfect will is. I have found that every time I pursue his pattern, and I don't follow my insecurities or wisdom from the world, I can't help but fall on my face in thankfulness towards God for his good, pleasing, and perfect will in my life. I always find myself thanking him for his will instead of my own.

Our will is usually a lot smaller, a lot safer, and a lot more comfortable than God's, but it is never as good! His will always causes us to become a little bit more brave than the time before, and I think it's because that is how he sees us. We are his brave, ferocious babes! He believes more in us than we believe in ourselves.

"...for God gave us a spirit not of fear but of power and love and self-control." (2 Timothy 1:7, ESV)

We must learn to stop putting ourselves down, calling our talents or gifts small, and telling ourselves that someone else can do it better. We shouldn't be shy about who we are! It's not serving the world or God for us to hold back. It doesn't matter if you are up at the front at church every Sunday or if you're cleaning the toilets. We all must learn to honor ourselves, honor the calling on our lives, thank God for it, and move forward in it. Otherwise, what are we really living for?

I'm not sure why we prefer to blend in than stick out. Maybe that's why God made a point to say in Matthew 5:14 that we are the light of the world and should not hide the light. He knew we would need to know that.

Being faithful with your calling every day, faithful with the gifts God has given you, faithful with following Jesus every day is how we live our lives with color, meaning, and purpose. If you're gifted in hospitality, be hospitable.

If you feel God has called you to sing and be on the worship team at church, it's silly for you to hide in the back for fear of not being as good as someone else. If you feel God has gifted you with an artistic ability, get artsy and put yourself out there. If you feel God has gifted you with hearing his voice, start to share what he speaks to you. Holding back, playing it small, and playing it safe will never do you any good. It's only when you let go of your fears, insecurities, and self-judgment to grab a hold of God's purpose for your life that you can live in your sweet spot and find meaning.

APPLICATION POINT:

Come to a place of honesty with yourself right now. Has the Holy Spirit been prompting you to do something that you've been too afraid to face because of what it might do to your reputation, convenient life, or comfort zone? Repent for ignoring what he was saying to you and ask the Holy Spirit to show you one small step to take today to move toward living electric blue!

Blueberry Buckwheat Bowl

INGREDIENTS:

3/4 cup dried buckwheat

1 Tbsp pure maple syrup

2 Tbsp nut butter

1/2 cup blueberries

1/2 cup strawberries

1 banana

1 Tbsp chia seeds

DIRECTIONS:

Soak the buckwheat overnight in 1 cup of water. In the morning, drain the buckwheat & rinse. Place 1/2 c of the buckwheat in a blender with the rest of the ingredients. Add an ice cube to make it cooler or use frozen berries so that it's chilled. Blend well. Place the mixture in a bowl and add the rest of the buckwheat on top. Add more fruit, dried fruit or seeds on top to your liking! Enjoy!

Spicy Avocado + Spinach Toast

INGREDIENTS:

2 slices of seeded whole grain bread

1/2 avocado

1/2 Tsp olive oil

1/4 Tsp garlic

1 small handful spinach (washed)

1/4 - 1/2 Tsp chili flakes

DIRECTIONS:

Toast bread to your liking. Then spread the avocado on the bread. In a sauce pan, sauté spinach, garlic and oil together for about a minute. Place the mixture on top of the toast. Sprinkle with the chili flakes, and enjoy!

slow and steady wins the race

D o you ever remember making a whirlpool when you went swimming as a kid? You'd jump into those round circular pools and start running along the edge. The faster you ran and the more you pushed through the water, the stronger the circular current went. By yourself, you can get the current going fairly strong, but if you have six other friends in the pool helping you push the water in the same circular direction, you can get the current going really fast. In fact, it can get so strong that eventually the water can become fiercer and quicker than you, and you lose your footing and get carried away in the circular current without even trying.

As I've gotten older, I realize most of us live life this way. We pack our schedules so full with church events, social events, work demands, meetings, and extra curricular activities that each thing we have on our calendar begins to push us into a flow of life that eventually causes us to lose our footing. Before you know it, our schedule is managing us rather than us managing our schedule.

In fact, I would say it always seems to be one of the most common things we complain about. We all talk about how we have no time, how we are so busy, how we wish we had more hours in a day. But in actuality, most of us prefer a crazy busy life. Don't think so? It's true. We like to always have something to do. As a society, we struggle to just sit and be still. Still don't believe me?

When you're at the doctor's office, waiting for your name to be called, what do you usually do without even thinking about it? Check your phone. You jump onto social media: Facebook, Twitter, Instagram, email. Even when we're able to take a minute to just sit there and wait, we can't! We have to keep the whirlpool going somehow. I am guilty of this myself. I have tried to just sit there and wait, without grabbing my phone, my iPad, Kindle, or any other electronic device, but it's like an itch I need to scratch.

If we were to actually stop the swirling whirlpool of to-do lists, social media, activities, and meetings, we might realize how being swept up into this whirlpool of life isn't healthy or beneficial for us. We need to learn to slow down.

BUSY VS. PURPOSEFUL

As Christians, the most important way we can practice slowing down in life is withdrawing from the world to get time alone with God. Interestingly enough, it is also one of the most neglected areas of the Christian life today. Even though we know we should, we hear it preached to us all the time, and we've maybe even felt a bit convicted about it at times, we still fail to do it. We don't mind going to church, going to events, going to coffee with each other because we are used to being on the go, go, go.

We like our busy lives.

When we're busy, it keeps us entertained, it makes us feel accomplished, and it gives us a sense of purpose. However, busyness is not always purposeful. In fact, sometimes our busyness can be a distraction from the things we're actually meant to be doing. We then tend to make excuses for why we can't do the things we're truly called to do. We default to saying, "I'm just too busy at the moment." And push it off to another more "convenient" time. But that time never really comes.

Remember the story of Mary and Martha? Martha thought she was doing the most important task of preparing a meal for Jesus, the Messiah. Many of us would certainly classify that as a very important night, having Jesus over for dinner. Can you imagine the stress, the busyness, the fussing around to get things just perfect for him? I don't blame Martha for getting frustrated with Mary for not helping. After all, she just sat there like a bum! However, Jesus told Martha that Mary had chosen the more important thing.

It's scary to think that because we're too busy working for him, we miss out on getting refreshed by him because we won't stop and slow down to receive it. The most important thing isn't our schedules, projects, and to-do lists. It's learning to slow down enough to listen to him. When we can listen to what he's saying, we discover what is and isn't important in each season of our lives. In return, this makes us more restful and more productive.

We could eliminate a lot of our frustration if we would only slow down long enough to ask Jesus, "What's the most important thing for me to do at this time?" Sometimes being productive is the right thing to do. Other times you might have a long list of things to do but it's more productive for you to rest and be with God and get lost in his presence.

THE IMPORTANCE OF WITHDRAWING TO BE WITH GOD

Jesus modeled a life of slowing down. Even in the midst

of the crowds, the demands, the needs, the pressure – he created time in his life to pray, reflect, and listen to God.

"After he had dismissed them, he went up on a mountainside by himself to pray. When evening came, he was there alone." (Matthew 14:23, NIV)

I truly believe that Jesus was only able to carry out his purpose the way he did because he made time to withdraw and be with his Father. He made a point to never allow the busyness of life to replace his time with God. He understood the genius behind it. He knew that when he did, burdens were lifted, clarity was brought to what he was doing, and refreshing from the Father was lavished upon him. He knew it was his lifeline—the secret ingredient to the life he lived.

When we withdraw to be with God, we are saying, "Lord, I am open to your voice. I am open to your correction. I am open to your wisdom. I am open to correcting any offenses in my heart. I am open to any blind spots I may have. I am open to hearing from you on whatever topic in

my life you'd like to speak to today because I trust you."
I love David's prayer in Psalm 139:23-24 (NIV), "Search me O Lord and know my heart, test me and know my anxious thoughts! See if there is any offensive way in me and lead me in that way everlasting!"

He was open to God speaking to him about anything that might need to be tweaked, changed, corrected, or done away with! When we choose to live like this before God, we live as healthier people because our hearts are clean, our minds are clear, and our souls are refreshed.

THE POWER OF STILLNESS

"Very early in the morning, while it was still dark, Jesus got up, left the house and went off to a solitary place, where he prayed." (Mark 1:35, NIV)

One of my favorite parts about this scripture is that Jesus went to a solitary place. Most of us can't remember the last time we chose to go to a solitary place with no cell phone, no radio, no TV, no internet. We are so used to our minds being filled with noise that if we don't withdraw to a quiet place, it can be difficult to hear God.

When I was about 16, I went off to a Christian summer camp. During my time there, the leaders decided we were going to practice an entire day of silence so we could better tune into the voice of God. We had to turn off and put away all our cell phones, the internet, and the TV – anything that would distract us. We weren't even allowed to speak to each other. It was total and complete silence out in the middle of nature. It was difficult at first. I wasn't sure what to do. I had never spent time like that with God before, and I was feeling a little uncomfortable. I was so used to the comfort of my busy life that when it came down to just God and me, I wasn't sure how I should act.

For most of us, a situation like that would be quite uncomfortable. In fact, it may be even a bit unnerving because we would rather pretend, hide, or deny any real issue we might need to confront in our lives. For me, it was a relationship I knew I wasn't supposed to be in, but convinced myself it was okay. Taking time to get away from all distractions forced me to become vulnerable and honest with myself and God. This let me confront that issue head on and deal with it.

When we create a space for God to speak and allow ourselves to be open to him speaking to us in whatever way he wants, it means we might need to actually deal with those inner heart issues. We might have to face up to our hurts, fears, or character issues. Maybe we are afraid God is going to tell us something we don't want to hear, like forgiving the person who hurt us. Maybe it could be stepping outside our comfort zone in a certain area or ending an unhealthy relationship. There are many reasons we might not want to tune into God's voice to our lives, but if we don't we're only hurting ourselves and hiding from the truth.

In John 14:6 (NIV), Jesus says, "I am the way and the truth and the life." When we come to him, he is able to show us the way – whether it's our destiny, direction on a situation, or strategy for a particular problem. Jesus reveals the truth, the truth of who we are in him. He also exposes lies we might be believing about ourselves or other people, and he shows us the truth about who he is. He brings us life when we slow down enough to connect with him. He refreshes us, gives us hope, heals our hearts, and bestows joy, peace, and love. These are all things that truly nourish us on the deepest level. He is life!

When slowing down and withdrawing to be with God becomes a routine part of your life, you begin to crave it. You will discover that Jesus can bring peace that surpasses understanding, he can relieve burdens off you, he can give you new perspectives, he can birth new dreams in you, and he can heal your heart. When you give Jesus your time and focus, you discover your energy source. Instead of living life nearly on empty, you live it full of the Spirit.

PRIORITIES, PRIORITIES, PRIORITIES!

I can remember a time when I was at work, and my manager discovered I was a holistic health coach. We would spend time talking about healthy recipes, exercise routines, and nutrition tips when work was slow. One day, as we were talking about these things, she shared with me that she knew she should be exercising but didn't have the time. She began to go through her daily routine from the moment she woke up until the time she went to bed. She explained that because she was so busy with work, kids, and other commitments, she simply did not have time to exercise. I could tell she was looking to me for some magical solution or insider tips on what to do. I just looked at her and said, "Well your problem is, you don't want to work out." And she looked surprised at my answer and pleaded, "Well, yes I do!" And I responded back, "No you don't. If you actually wanted to work out, you'd make time to do it. You just don't want to."

She stared at me for a moment, thinking about what I said and then eventually answered back, "You're right." The next day she came to work and told me she went home and exercised that night. From that point forward, she incorporated healthy movement into her regular lifestyle.

I use this story to illustrate the fact that it isn't a time issue, it's a priority issue. We will always do what is important to us. It's unhelpful to lie to ourselves and use our schedules as excuses for why we can't slow down. In reality, we can't afford to not make time.

SELF-CARE

Another misunderstood area we should incorporate into our daily lives to help us slow down is self-care. I find that because the Bible tells us it's better to give than to receive (Acts 20:35), that we should be selfless (Phil 2:3), and we should serve others (Gal 5:13), we feel guilty for taking "me" time. We often tend to neglect ourselves – especially as women who seek to look after our spouses, children, and others – we rarely spend money, time, or energy on ourselves.

When we fail to give attention to our own needs, we become overly emotional, worn down, drained, and burnt out. We might be soaring spiritually, but our soul is withering.

"Dear friend, I pray that you may enjoy good health and that all may go well with you, even as your soul is getting along well." (3 John 1:2, NIV)

God wants our souls to prosper. We are a spirit, who has a soul, and lives in a body. It's important that we look after our soul, and we do that through self-care. Most of us claim we are too busy to make time for ourselves. In the same way we must not neglect spending time with God, we must not neglect to take time for ourselves.

I can remember when my husband and I bought our first house. After we moved all our stuff in, it was now time to put everything away. We spent hours cleaning the house, putting things away, setting furniture up, hanging decorations on the walls, and I was becoming exhausted. My husband decided we should take a break and sit down on the couch to watch a movie together. As he sat down, I continued to unpack boxes. He asked me to come sit down with him. I expressed to him that we didn't have time to sit down, that we needed to get things done. I'm the type of person who hates a mess, so these boxes everywhere were driving me crazy. He insisted that I watch the movie. In my mind, that was the absolute last thing I wanted to do. However, my husband knew I needed it. He came over to me, grabbed me, and sat me down on the couch. As I sat there, my eyes weren't on the T.V, they were scanning the room as I was contemplating what needed to go where. It was at that point that he grabbed my face, looked me in the eye, and said, "You need to relax." He's really good for me, thank God!

There will always be the laundry, the dishes, the vacuuming, the bathroom needing cleaning, people who need our help, and things we could be doing. And we can run ourselves into the ground by trying to keep up with it all unless we learn to slow down and make time to relax.

What do you enjoy? Long walks? Massages? Going out to dinner? Getting your nails done? Fishing? Watching your favorite show? Gardening? Buying yourself a big bouquet of flowers? Getting your hair done? It's important that you make time to do things you enjoy. It is not selfish or unspiritual for you to give yourself a bit of attention when you need it. In fact, I would argue it's just as important as going to your child's parent-teacher meeting or getting the laundry done because it helps keep your soul prospering.

We must have balance in everything we do. Please don't think I'm saying that you should go blow all your cash and spend all your time on yourself, however, you should schedule time in your regular calendar for "slow down" time, and this will look different for each person.

Now, some of you might be wondering about the balance between taking care of ourselves and being overly concerned with our appearance.

"Don't be concerned about the outward beauty of fancy hairstyles, expensive jewelry, or beautiful clothes. You should clothe yourselves instead with the beauty that comes from within, the unfading beauty of a gentle and quiet spirit, which is so precious to God. This is how the holy women of old made

themselves beautiful. They put their trust in God and accepted the authority of their husbands." (1 Peter 3:3-5, NLT)

This scripture says our beauty should not come from clothes, jewelry, or hairstyles. It doesn't say don't wear them, rather our beauty should originate from inside of us! We are to understand that we are beautiful because of our Christ-like nature. However, to wear a new outfit, have your hair done nicely, and buy yourself a new necklace is okay, as long as your identity isn't coming from those things.

God wants us to enjoy our lives. He wants us to take time to smell the roses. He wants us to take care of ourselves. He is a good father, and in the same way a dad wants his daughters to be blessed, taken care of, and feeling good, so does our heavenly dad. So treat yourself regularly to something that you enjoy and learn how to slow down. This way you can enjoy the benefits of a fuller and healthier life.

APPLICATION POINT:

Take time this week to sit down in total silence to just be with God. How does it feel? Do you notice yourself itching to reach for your phone? Is it uncomfortable to do nothing? Sit there long enough until you can push past the uncomfortable stillness and come to a place where you start to let go of what you feel is "important." Just enjoy being with God.

Sweet Potato Cakes

INGREDIENTS:

4 Sweet Potatoes

2 Tbsp flour

2 Garlic Cloves

2 Tbsp tomato puree

Fresh chopped cilantro

1 tsp ground cumin

1 tsp chili flakes

1 Tbsp tahini

1 lime (juiced)

Avocado (optional)

Rocket/Spinach/Dark Leafy Greens (optional)

salt and pepper

olive oil

DIRECTIONS:

Peel the sweet potatoes and cut them into cubes. Steam the sweet potatoes for about 15 minutes until soft.

Preheat the oven to 420 F.

cont'd ▶

cont'd

Place the steamed potatoes in a bowl and mash together until smooth. Add in the flour, tomato puree, garlic, cilantro, cumin, chili flakes tahini, lime juice, salt and pepper. Mix it all together.

With your hands, create 4 potato cakes and place on an oiled baking tray. Dust each cake with a bit of flour. Bake the cakes for about 20 minutes until the top turns golden brown. Serve the cakes on a bed of your favorite greens and add avocado with lime if you'd like! I usually add a bit more chili flakes to spice it up!

Pear, Pecan, and Goat Cheese Salad

INGREDIENTS:

1 Pear cut up

Spinach

Arugula

Pecan pieces

Goat cheese crumbles

2 Tbsp Balsamic Vinegar

Cracked Black Pepper

DIRECTIONS:

Combine a generous amount of spinach and arugula together. Throw in the remaining ingredients and enjoy!

it's a wonderful life

N ot too long ago, my husband and I felt God speak to us about moving from America to the United Kingdom to plant a church. After we prayed about it and felt it was the right decision, we assumed we would be there in 6 months time. We reasoned that if God had spoken to us about it, he meant as soon as possible!

However, from the initial time he spoke to us until our actual move date, it ended up being a year and a half. Not only was it much longer than we anticipated; it was a year full of unfortunate events. My car began to have several serious issues that cost us lots of money. After we replaced almost every major part, I was hit by a drunk driver. We had to scrap the car and get a new one. The house we bought had mold issues we could not seem to solve, our washing machine continued to break, and our heat didn't work upstairs. The company my husband worked for laid him off. Once he landed another job and things started to improve, that company had to lay him off. They were having trouble making payroll and couldn't afford to pay their employees. This happened only a few days before Christmas. It was one thing after another going wrong, and it was a trying time to say the least.

For most of my life I have been pretty fortunate. Although my parents weren't sleeping on a bed of money every night, I was never aware of any financial struggles we might have had. I'm very thankful for that, and I never struggled to believe God would provide for me. No matter what I did, whatever drastic decision I made, God always backed me up with his provision and favor.

During this time, I wondered if we were doing something wrong. At times, I questioned whether we were making the right decision to move. Why would all these issues arise when we were trying to do what God asked us to do? I had never been through such a difficult season of financial struggle in my life.

Eventually, things began to come together and we were only weeks away from making our big move. I can remember driving the car, and I knew deep down that I was worried about how this transition was going to go. Would my husband find a good job? Will we find a good place to live? Will we make good friends? Will we have enough? Will we be ok? These questions were percolating in my heart underneath the surface for some time. I began to pray and ask God to speak to me about what this new move would entail.

I prayed for what seemed like a long time and heard nothing.

At one point, I began to think, "Melissa, stop kidding yourself! You really think you can move to another country after the year you've just had? You have hardly been able to save! This could be another year of even worse struggle!" In that moment, I felt myself going into a downward spiral. My mind started to give into doubt and fear. In an attempt to keep myself from letting my emotions get the best of me, I blurted out, "Lord, I know it's just going to be wonderful!"

And then He spoke to me. The word "wonderful" hit my ears like a massive church choir singing "Hallelujah!" He said, "That's exactly what it's going to be: wonderful! Full of wonder!"

Everything inside of me lifted and I could feel myself beaming. All my worries fell to the ground, and faith filled my heart. "Full of wonder! Full of his goodness! Full of his blessing in surprising ways! Full of life!" I kept repeating it to myself. "Wonderful" became life to me as the Holy Spirit breathed on it and began to speak excitement into my heart. It was wonderful!

FOCUS ON THE WONDER

Many of us have forgotten that God truly is a wonderful God. It could be years and years of difficult circumstances, sickness, bad relationships, or unanswered questions that cloud our eyes to see the truth of who he is: a good, kind, wonder-working God all the time. We have forgotten he can turn our situations around in a heartbeat. He moves in power and love, he is for us, he loves to surprise us with good things, he can do anything, he is a miracle-worker, and he is good all the time. Sometimes we fail to see God in that way, and we don't live our lives with an expectation of his goodness because of negative events in life.

I am amazed at the story of Moses and the Israelites. Moses rescues an entire nation of people from bondage and slavery through many miraculous signs and wonders and eventually parts an entire sea (Exodus 14:21). Talk about living a life of wonder!

Shortly after that, though, when they were traveling through the wilderness, the Israelites start to complain, grumble, and murmur about Moses and their situation (Exodus 17:3). Every time they complained about lack of water or food, the Lord would miraculously provide, like water from a rock (Exodus 17:6) or manna from heaven (Exodus 16:4). Sadly, even after all of that, the Israelites still questioned, "Is the Lord among us or not?" (Exodus 17:7, NIV).

The Israelites focused so much on their wilderness moments, they failed to see God working wonders around them. In fact, they complained and grumbled about their hardships so much that it eventually killed them. A whole generation never entered the Promised Land, but instead died in the wilderness.

All of us face wilderness seasons or situations in our lives, but we are never meant to focus on them.

You were created to live in the wonder not wondering. Wondering like the Israelites did, and asking, "Is the Lord among us or not?" is never a good place to be. It's a place of doubt and unbelief. Doubt and unbelief will cause you to stay in a wilderness mentality, and if you don't deal with it, it will eventually kill you.

The scriptures are packed with promises from God, saying, "He will never leave you nor forsake you." (Deuteronomy 31:6, NIV). In Ephesians, he also tells us he can do immeasurably more than what we can ask, think, or imagine. Regardless of what we're going through, God is always wonderful. We must choose to see him, focus on the promises he gives us in his word, and thank him for the good things he is doing in our lives. We must choose to believe in a good, wonder-working God.

RECONNECT WITH YOUR INNER CHILD

In Matthew 18:2, the disciples ask Jesus who the greatest one in the kingdom of heaven is, and Jesus responds with this: "He called a little child to him, and placed the child among them. And he said: 'Truly I tell you, unless you change and become like little children, you will never enter the kingdom of heaven.'" (NIV)

Children live with their head in the sky. They believe in fairies, magic powers, imaginary friends, and Santa Claus. What Jesus was saying here is the kingdom of heaven is seen and experienced when you live in a place of belief like a child. You cannot experience it, you cannot enter it, and you cannot see it when you've grown up and become realistic.

Adults get life. There comes a point in our lives or perhaps it occurs over time as we grow up, where we stop believing in Santa, mermaids, and fairy tales. We get jobs, we pay the bills, we clean the house – we experience real life. Sometimes we can even become hardened by it. It's not just the responsibilities of our everyday life that wear on us. It's the really difficult life circumstances that can cause us to lose our childlike faith. We can lose our wonder.

The disciples wanted to know who would be the greatest, In our world today, people measure greatness through worldly success: our position at work, the kind of house we have, the car we drive, the size of our ministry, the clothes we wear, and the vacations we take. I'd imagine the disciples had expected Jesus to say something equivalent to their idea of worldly success. For us it would be those who have worked hard, gone on to get a college education, and live in a big fancy house with nice things. They will be the greatest. But Jesus didn't say that. Success in that sense wasn't as important to Jesus. He was making a point to say that the most valuable thing is becoming like a child.

There is nothing wrong with having worldly success, in fact we should strive to be successful in our world so that we can better influence it. However, Jesus was wanting to make a point that becoming child-like, trusting, and believing is the most important thing.

If we are going to enter the kingdom of God, we must become like little children. Children expect that when dinnertime comes, there will be a hot meal waiting for them. Children expect that when their shoes become too tight, they will get a new pair. Children don't worry about a thing, but they live a life of expectation and belief that it's all going to be taken care of.

Likewise, we are not called to be realistic, over-burdened

adults who worry, question, and doubt. We are called to trust our heavenly Father and expect good things to come to us. We're called to live in a place where the belief in miracles is possible, healing is available, provision is accessible, and answers are given to us by our heavenly Father.

That is the reality of what we can live in, if we believe.

Did you know secular health experts say that having a belief in a higher power is beneficial to one's health? They might use phrases like, "the Universe will manifest good things for me" or "the God of the universe knows what I need." Either way, we were created to be people of faith. These health experts have concluded that most people who believe in a higher power are less stressed, worry less, and are happier people. It is becoming more popular for doctors and holistic health practitioners to encourage their clients to develop and cultivate a spiritual practice because they see people's health improve.

These people are simply choosing to believe their needs will be taken care of by something more powerful than them. Thankfully the God we serve really does that. We must learn to really believe it.

I BELIEVE IN MIRACLES!

The more and more I grow in my walk with the Lord, the more I find that sometimes it's not the challenging life situations that cause us to lose the wonder, but it's the sheer familiarity of this whole Christian life that does. Christians who have been walking with God for years, and who have been faithful by continuing in their journey can unknowingly become all too familiar with the Bible, the church, and God.

Mark 6:1-6 describes when Jesus returns to his hometown after starting his ministry. He has been healing many people and performing many miracles. The sad thing is, the people in his hometown were familiar with him, and because of their familiarity it says, "he could not do any miracles there, except lay his hands on a few sick people and heal them. He was amazed at their lack of faith." (NIV)

Have you gotten so accustomed to and familiar with this Christian life that you have lost the wonder? These people lost the wonder, the expectation, and the faith which affected their ability to receive all Jesus could offer. Jesus still healed a few sick people who were amongst him, but he probably could have done a lot more if they had believed. But because they were familiar with who he was—a carpenter—and he was in his hometown, they couldn't see the miracle-working Jesus. The truth of who he was. All they could see was who they were familiar with.

Perhaps you've lost the expectation that God can move in power at any time in your life. If we call ourselves "believers," then we must believe. It's good and healthy for us to put our trust in someone greater than ourselves. We aren't called to live this life with the weight of the world on our shoulders. But we are called to be child-like and believe that God will take care of all our needs at the right time.

KEEPING YOUR LUSTER

"Blessed are the pure in heart, for they will see God." (Matthew 5:8, NIV)

It's so important that we keep a pure heart before God. The scripture above tells us those who keep a pure heart are blessed because they shall see God!

When we keep hurt, bitterness, doubt, fear, or unforgiveness in our hearts, they blind us from seeing God for who he really is – God! We lose sight of his love, kindness, peace, joy, wonder, and goodness because junk is in the way.

One of the best ways we can stay in a place of wonder is by keeping our hearts clean.

I can remember a time when I was first saved; God was so big to me! It was the first time I had really seen him for who he was. He is exciting, loving, and kind. I wondered how people could not possibly trust him with their whole lives because he was God. I really saw this miraculous God.

He was so real to me that I felt that I needed to tell everyone about him. I went in the supermarket, the gas station, the mall, my university—everywhere! I wanted people to see what I saw.

Then after a year or so, for the first time in my Christian walk, I experienced some personal hurt from within the church I was part of. I had misinterpreted good intentions for evil, and it caused a root of disappointment to form in my heart. I did not know how to properly deal with it, so it eventually turned into anger, then bitterness.

I will never forget the day one of my church leaders sat me down to talk. He looked at me and said, "Melissa, you've lost your luster."

Those words really shocked me. I knew he was right. In just a few short months, I had gone from a bright, smiley, optimistic, and faith-filled girl, to a critical, judgmental, and paranoid Christian. It was at that point, I realized I had stopped seeing God because all I saw was hurt. I had to make the decision to give the whole situation over to God and repent for my bad attitudes. After I dealt with myself, I started to come back to a place of faith and wonder again.

It can sometimes be so easy for offense to happen. People aren't perfect. Miscommunication can happen, often. Things can be misinterpreted. It's life! However, when we don't deal with our own hearts, we can lose our luster.

PULL OUT ROTTEN ROOTS

It is vital that we deal with those root issues of hurt, bitterness, or doubt in our lives. The Bible clearly says to get rid of it all, and instead be kind, compassionate, and forgiving towards one another (Ephesians 4:31). Jesus made a point to tell us that it is unhealthy for any of us to hold onto those feelings. It doesn't do any good holding on to unforgiveness towards someone, bitterness, or rage; it only ends up hurting ourselves. It's not always easy to stay kind, compassionate, or forgiving towards everyone, but it is one of the best and healthiest things you can do for yourself spiritually.

If we are going to get back to a place of wonder, luster, and trust, we must choose to deal with those issues in our heart that we would like to sweep under the rug. Not dealing with those things keeps us stuck in them. God never wants any of us stuck or hurt, which is why we must face those problems no matter how painful they might be.

GOD HAS SOMETHING WONDERFUL IN STORE FOR YOU!

God doesn't promise us a problem-free life. In fact, Jesus tells us in John 16:33, "In this world you will have trouble." (NIV) He actually promises that we will face difficult circumstances. While some people might find that unnerving, I find it comforting because Jesus understands us when we go through difficult times. He empathizes with us.

Fortunately though, Jesus never puts a period on our

difficult circumstances. He could have chosen to finish that verse right there but he didn't. He finishes the scripture with, "But take heart, for I have overcome the world!" Even in the midst of our toughest life issues, God is always up to something wonderful.

If we are going to live a wonderful life, we must choose to focus on the good things God is doing in our lives not the difficulties we might be facing. They could be the big wonder-filled things or small wonder-filled things. He cares about the big as much as the small, and we should too.

Come back to a place of childlikeness. You're called to live in the kingdom of God every day. Come back to a place of faith in the miraculous, trust in a good God, and believe in His power because it is, after all, a wonderful life.

APPLICATION POINT 1:

Pray and ask the Holy Spirit if you have any rotten roots in your heart such as bitterness, unforgiveness, anger, or frustration towards anyone or anything. If you do, repent to the Lord for holding on it and then renounce those feelings and ask the Lord to soften your heart so you can begin to come to a place of wonder again.

APPLICATION POINT 2:

I challenge you to ask God what wonderful things he has in store for you this year. Perhaps write a list of things you'd like to see happen in your life. Things like, how many people you'd like to see give their lives to God, people you'd like to see healed, and situations you'd like to see turned around. Make a big list and take off all the limitations of what your brain thinks is possible. Remember, we serve a wonder-working God. It's time to lift up our faith and believe for big things!

Black Bean Soup

INGREDIENTS:

1 1/2 cups black beans

1 red and yellow bell pepper

1 red onion

1 Tbsp Mexican tinga paste

4 cups spicy vegetable stock (or add your own chilies)

1 can diced tomatoes

1 clove chopped garlic

Cilantro

Avocado

4 Corn Tortillas

Olive Oil

Sea Salt

DIRECTIONS:

In a pan, sauté the onions and peppers together for 3 minutes. Once finished, combine the beans, Mexican paste, garlic, tomatoes, peppers, and onions into a pot. Add the vegetable stock and boil the mixture. Once

cont'd ▶

cont'd

boiling, bring to a simmer, and let simmer for 15 minutes. While cooking, spread the olive oil on both sides to the tortillas. Sprinkle with a bit of sea salt. Then cut the tortillas into triangle shapes. Spread onto a cooking sheet and put in the oven at 400F. Check on them every 5 minutes until crispy.

Finally, top with the cilantro and avocado, and top your soup with some homemade tortilla chips.

CHAPTER 5

life is a party and you're invited

A few years ago, I went into a sports shop to buy a gift for someone. I was with my husband, and I was on a mission. I had a very full schedule of things I needed to do in a short amount of time. I was in no mood to waste time. As my husband and I walked into the store, I bee-lined it to find a particular item.

As we walked past the basketballs and basketball hoops, my husband grabbed a ball, started to dribble, and shot the ball into one of the baskets. I ignored him and continued to search for the item. We walked past the canoes, and he got in pretending to paddle through the store and invited me to a join him in his little adventure.

But, I continued to search for the item. We walked past the rugby balls, and he started throwing the ball in the air. At this point, I started to get annoyed by his clear lack of time sensitivity. I just wanted to get in and get out.

When I finally found the item and was on my way out, I sharply said to him, "Keane! Let's go!" It was at that point, he ran towards me, threw me over his shoulder and began parading me around the store! I began to yell, "Keane! Put me down! Stop this! You're acting ridiculous! We need to go!" He continued thinking it was absolutely hysterical. He then stepped onto an escalator, which was in the center of the store, and we started to go up with me over his shoulder and my butt in the air! I continued to kick and sternly tell him to put me down. I felt so embarrassed!

As we reached the top, he finally put me on my feet. Just as I was about to tell him off, he said to me, "Melissa, just enjoy life!" And walked away.

I stood there speechless. I knew it was a God moment.

I stood there taking those words in, "Melissa, just enjoy life." I realized, I missed out on having a good time with my fun-loving husband because I was so wrapped up in my own agenda.

God began to speak to me that I had a tendency to do this all the time. I was so concerned with working, being productive, accomplishing, being responsible, and making sure things were clean and in order all the time. I was bothered if my husband had a different opinion than mine. I was bothered if the dishes were a mess for too long. I was bothered if things didn't go my way. I was just bothered! God was trying to get my attention so I could enjoy this life he had given me. Sadly, I really didn't even know how.

I was so concerned with the end goal that I was missing out on the fun, the enjoyment, the party.

JOY MEANS STRENGTH

"The joy of the Lord is my strength." (Nehemiah 8:10, NIV)

I had no idea how to be happy if things didn't go my way. I could be joyful if my husband did what I wanted to do, if I had gotten everything done the way I wanted it done, if God was doing things in my life that I understood. If all those things were in order, I was a joyful girl. If any one of those things was off, I was a grumpy, annoyed, tired, and worn out girl.

The joy of the Lord was only my strength when I agreed with what was happening in my life. However, that's not how that scripture goes. It's pretty straightforward: "the joy of the Lord is my strength" period. So the question then becomes, how can we learn to live in joy all the time regardless of what we think or feel?

JOY IS A CHOICE

When my husband and I were trying to sell our house, we had issues with it for months. After a long process of trying to rent it out, keep renters, and make sure all the issues in it were fixed, we finally decided to sell. Then one day, my realtor phoned and told us that someone put an offer on the table above our asking price. My husband and I were so excited! I can remember thinking, "Finally! Something is starting to go our way." As the days went on and the time to sign the papers drew closer, we began to anticipate our big break more and more.

A short time later, I received a text message from our realtor that just said, "The buyers have walked."

In that moment everything in me wanted to throw my hands in the air and scream. In an instant the Holy Spirit arrested my heart and brought this verse to my mind:

"Consider it pure joy, my brothers and sisters, whenever you face trials of many kinds, because you know that the testing of your faith produces perseverance. Let perseverance finish its work so that you may be mature and complete, not lacking anything." (James 1:2-4, NIV)

I thought for a moment about what this meant. I said to myself, "Wait. When you face a trial, God says to count it as joy. So, a trial means I'm supposed to be happy about that? Count it all joy?" As I stood there and tried making sense of this whole thing in my head, a text message came through on my phone from my husband asking, "Are you okay?" I paused for a moment with this verse resounding in my heart and replied back, "I'm counting it... joy!" I continued working in peace for the rest of the day.

I learned something incredibly valuable that day. I can't control the world. I can't control people. I can't always control my circumstances. I can't control certain outcomes. The only thing I can control is myself, and if that's the case, I'd rather choose to be happy. I have held onto that verse since then. At any point in my life when I have come against a trial, instead of getting all wound up about it, I have learned to consider it pure joy.

I do this not because it's a "positive thinking" tactic, but because the Bible says that when our faith is being tested and we persevere through it, we become more mature and lack nothing. One thing I certainly want to become is a mature believer in Christ, not a whiner! So when trials come, I've learned they are an opportunity to discover a new way God wants to reveal himself to me at that time. When we go through a time of our faith being tested financially, we can come to know God as our provider in a greater way. When we go through a time of heartache, we can experience the Holy Spirit as our comforter in a deeper way. Even in times of stretching, we get to catch another facet of the beauty of God and grow to know him more.

No one of us enjoys having her faith tested or learning perseverance due to unpleasant circumstances in life. Through these we become a stronger, more complete, and more mature believer (James 1:4).

I certainly don't believe God ever brings destruction, sickness, or death into any of our lives. In fact, John 10:10 says, "the devil comes to steal, kill, and destroy but I have come that they may have life in abundance." We all face seasons where trials will come our way, and we must choose joy to get through them. It's a weapon of the Holy Spirit to keep us strong, and we must learn to use it!

Normally a situation like the one I just shared would have ruined the rest of my day. I would have complained, been upset about it, and allowed the devil to have a field day with me, but I just chose to let go and trust God. I've learned to refuse to live angry and instead count it all joy. I no longer want to live life as a control freak. I want to learn to know and believe that God has my life in his hands. He is God, and I am not.

JOY CAN BE CULTIVATED

Paul encourages us in this saying:

"I am not saying this because I am in need, for I have learned to be content whatever the circumstances. I know what it is to be in need, and I know what it is to have plenty. I have learned the secret of being content in any and every situation, whether well fed or hungry, whether living in plenty or in want." (Philippians 4:11-12, NIV)

When Paul wrote this, I cannot imagine the process he had to go through to be able to say, "I have learned to be content whatever the circumstances." In a world that is always telling us you can do better, become better, and have better, what a wonderful thing to be able to say, "I've learned to be content with whatever" and to trust God in any and every circumstance. To know he is faithful and will work all things together for good, to simply learn that whether everything goes your way or nothing goes your way, you find out what it means to be content no matter what. Joy is found in that place.

One fruit of the Spirit is joy. I truly never thought that happy people worked at being happy. To be honest, I thought that happy people just had perfect lives. I was naive to think that. Especially when most of the time, people only allow us to see what they want us to see on social media in pictures or Facebook statuses.

Joy is something that must be cultivated. That is why the Bible calls it a "fruit" of the spirit. In the same way a seed is planted into the ground and needs consistent water, sunshine, and weeding in order for it to grow and become a ripe juicy piece of fruit, we must cultivate joy on purpose. It's a choice. A decision. Something that we must grow in.

It's actually a comforting thought to know that if you are lacking joy, you can make the choice to grow in it in the same way you would with diligence or kindness. You are not a victim of your circumstances, you are a powerful person who can become skilled at being joyful. What an empowering thought!

Jesus is the happiest person I know. He is never worried, annoyed, sour-faced, or grumpy. The Bible says that God sits in the heavens and laughs (Psalm 2:4). He is happy, and we're called to be like Him. The famous Proverbs 31 woman is described as one who, "is clothed with strength and dignity; she can laugh at the days to come" (Proverbs 31:25, NIV). How wonderful is that? Instead of worrying about our future, what if we simply throw our heads back and laugh in full confidence in the goodness of our God!

We aren't more spiritual when we worry more. We're more spiritual when we're light and carefree. Even when God burdens our hearts for people or situations going on in the world, we are supposed to feel love and compassion. Then, we can pray and reach out to those people while allowing God's grace to abound in us, so we can live light and free. Jesus tells us his yoke is easy and his burden is light (Matthew 11:30). No one is going to want what we have if we look miserable and heavy all the time. We must learn to grow in joy and have it ooze out from us to everyone we meet. We are called to be salt and light. We should be known as the happiest people on the planet!

WE'RE CALLED TO BE A PEOPLE OF PRAISE!

Throughout the Bible, God reminds us to rejoice, praise, and give thanks. In fact, he says that he turns our mourning into dancing (Psalm 30:11). There have been times when I've been learning to grow in joy, and I've forced myself to smile even though I didn't feel like it. I would repeat to myself, "You turn my mourning into dancing!" I would read verses that told me to give thanks and praise. Even if I felt dreary on the inside, I would still find something to praise him for,

We might enter the kingdom of God with burdens and hurt, but we're not called to stay like that. Whatever has you mad, wound up, and upset, let it go and give it to God! He truly specializes in turning our sorrows into joy if we let him.

When I was growing up, I struggled quite a bit with depression. It's a terrible mental illness for people to have. I was on medication, saw counselors, and tried many things to get my "happy" back. When I gave my heart to Jesus, I can remember feeling so wonderful, I knew that was how I was supposed to feel every single day.

As I continued to walk with the Lord, there were times when my depression would try to sneak back up and pull me down. I remember sitting in my living room one day praying to God to help me not go down this slippery slope of negative thought patterns and depression.

As I was in prayer, God showed me a picture. It was of an enormous hot air balloon. Inside the balloon was a massive spark of fire blazing upward, trying to propel the balloon upward for lift off. However, the hot air balloon was still tied to the ground. The fire inside continued to blow hot air upward to lift this huge balloon up into the air but the balloon remained stuck to the ground. God spoke to me and said, "I've given you everything you need to soar, now YOU must cut the ties."

It was the first time I realized I needed to do something. I needed to take responsibility for my feelings and my faith. I was praying that God would do something for me, but he was telling me I needed to do something. I needed to start believing the Bible, declaring the truth over myself, choosing joy, and learning to take captive my negative thoughts. Those were the ties that still held me to the ground. Once I began to do this, I started to soar!

We are co-laborers with Christ. We must work with the Holy Spirit to see the power of God released in our lives. He's not going to drag us along; we must move with him! This transformation did not happen overnight. It was a process, and I'm still learning every day, but I've gotten better and better at cultivating joy in my life. While I have compassion for those who still struggle with this horrible mental illness, I found that the joy of the Lord has been my strength, and depression no longer holds me down. Glory to God!

We're not called to be these weighed-down, uptight, controlling, overly-serious, overly-sensitive women! We're called to live care-free and light-hearted with hearts full of joy and peace every day. It's for freedom that Christ set us free (Galatians 5:1).

THE JOY OF SAYING "NO"

As God started to reveal to me joy was something I could grow in, He began to speak to me about the way I acted around friends and family in my life. If someone needed something, I said yes. If plans needed to change, I said yes. If someone had a different opinion about something, I went with it. I thought because I said yes all the time I was an easy going person. But I wasn't. Saying yes only made me a people-pleaser, and in the end, it got me more upset, uptight, and frustrated because I was too busy pleasing everyone.

It wasn't until I learned to say "no" sometimes and stop being so concerned about everyone else's happiness that I was finally able to relax within myself and make wise decisions. There is nothing wrong with creating healthy boundaries in our lives so that we stay sane. It is absolutely impossible to keep everyone happy all the time. Plus, there is not a single verse in the Bible that asks us to do that.

Life is too short not to enjoy it. You will always struggle to enjoy your own God-given party if you can't learn to enjoy yourself first. You are who you are, and it's time for you to embrace yourself instead of wishing you were like someone else. Envy and jealousy will always be party poopers to your own self-celebration. They will always tell you that the blessing that is over someone else's life will never happen for you. Choose to reject envy and jealousy because they are always lies meant to destroy our joy. God has wonderful and fantastic things planned for each one of us, so make it a goal to enjoy your destiny. Learn to laugh at yourself instead of beating yourself up. Enjoy your goofy quirks instead of hating yourself for them.

Don't spend so much of your time and effort getting somewhere in life, so that you miss out on those special moments with those you love. Play more with your kids instead of cleaning up their messes. Learn to love your husband exactly the way he is instead of always trying to change him. Learn to forgive and love your friends and make time to have some fun in your life.

Learn to take responsibility for your own happiness instead of blaming it on other people or life situations. Joy is a decision every single day, and I encourage you to make the choice to live joyful regardless of anything else.

Your life can be a party at any time you choose to have one, and I believe God is inviting you to have one!

APPLICATION POINT:

Make a decision right now to count it all joy. It's easier to read about than actually do, but the Bible promises that if we count it all joy when we're facing a trial, we will become mature and complete. No matter what situation you're facing or what circumstance you're in, choose to trust God and count it joy.

Easy Quinoa + Chickpea Chicken Curry

INGREDIENTS

1 cup quinoa rinsed & drained

1 can (400ml) coconut milk

1 can (400ml) diced tomatoes

3 Tbsp curry powder (note: curry powders vary in heat. If in doubt, go with less, and add more later)

2 Tbsp tomato paste

2 Tbsp coconut oil (or other vegetable oil)

1 large onion

1 clove garlic, minced

1 carrot, diced

1 can (400g) chickpeas, drained or 1lb cubed chicken sautéed

2 large handfuls of chopped spinach or kale

½ tsp crushed red chili pepper

Salt and pepper

Cilantro (fresh coriander) (optional)

cont'd ▶

cont'd

DIRECTIONS:

In a medium saucepan, mix quinoa, coconut milk, diced tomatoes (with juice), curry powder, and tomato paste, and bring to a boil. Bring heat to lowest setting, cover the saucepan, and let it simmer until quinoa is ready, about 15 minutes.

While the quinoa is cooking, in a frying pan, cook oil over medium heat and stir fry the garlic and onion until translucent. Add the carrot, and sauté for a couple minutes.

Add the chickpeas (or sautéed chicken), and cook for another couple minutes. Add the spinach/kale, and cook until wilted, about a minute. Mix the veggies with the quinoa, season with salt, pepper, and crushed red chili pepper, and garnish with cilantro before serving.

Pepper + Hummus Wrap

INGREDIENTS:

1/4 Red Pepper

1/4 Yellow Pepper

1/4 Green Pepper

1/2 cup Spinach

2 Tbsp Hummus

1 Seeded Whole Wheat Tortilla

DIRECTIONS:

Slice the peppers into strips. Sauté them on the skillet for 3 minutes on medium. Spread the hummus in the middle of the tortilla. Then, evenly spread the spinach over the hummus. Layer the sautéed peppers onto the bed of spinach. Fold the sides of the tortilla in, and roll the tortilla. Place the tortilla in a Panini maker or on a skillet to sear the bottom. Slice in two, and enjoy!

CHAPTER 6

planted flowers flourish

God wants each one of us to blossom and flourish into who he has called us to be. One of the most important aspects of a healthy Christian life is to be planted in a local church. Making Jesus our Lord and Savior is only the beginning of our walk with God. Committing ourselves to a local church helps us fully walk out our calling. When we are planted in a body of believers, we are able to put spiritual roots down to be nurtured, looked after, fed, and flourish in God.

When I was growing up, I was a Christian, but I didn't go to church. No one in my family was saved. I came into a personal relationship with Jesus when I heard the gospel at a Christian camp at a young age. Every summer I would go to this camp and be surrounded by Christians who loved the Lord. I heard the preached word, I went to my camp leaders for advice about real life issues, and I grew spiritually every summer. I always felt so built up when I would leave. At the end of camp, I thought more clearly, felt equipped to take on life, and was inspired to live right! Sadly though, after a month being at home, I'd be struggling with my same issues again: depression, broken relationships, negative attitudes, and confusion about my life and purpose.

It was not until years later when I made the decision to fully make Jesus the Lord of my life and committed myself to a good church that I actually began to see a positive and lasting transformation in my life. Once I planted myself in a body of believers, I was positioned to receive God's best. I aligned myself with what He says instead of what was easy or convenient for me.

We are not called to "church-hop," only go when we feel like it, or only watch a preacher on the T.V. We are called to get connected to a solid local church and plant ourselves there by creating relationships with the people and serving in some capacity.

I am not a master in the garden. I *do* understand that in order for a flower to blossom, it must be able to put its roots into the soil, so they can go down deep and grow. If a flower is constantly being uprooted and replanted in different soil, the flower isn't going to be able to grow to be tall, strong, and healthy. The church is a gift from God that helps us flourish in our lives. This passage clearly shows the benefits of being planted:

"They will be planted in the house of the Lord,
they will flourish in the courts of our God.
They will still bear fruit in old age,
they will stay fresh and green,
proclaiming, "The Lord is upright;
he is my Rock, and there is no wickedness in him."
(Psalm 92:13-15, NIV)

RELATIONSHIPS

One of the main reasons why being part of a healthy local church is so essential in a Christians life is because we are not meant to do this Christian life alone! When God created Adam, there came a point when God saw that it wasn't good for man to be alone, so he created Eve (Genesis 2:18). God knew and understood that while Adam had the most intimate relationship with God, he still needed human relationships.

In the same way, God hasn't called anyone to live this Christian life in solitude. Many people think that they don't need to go to church. They believe "just me and God" is enough. However, in the same way Adam needed human relationships and an intimate walk with God, so do we. Because we were created to be relational.

The problem is, though, too many Christians form their closest relationships with people who are not believers and struggle to live in a place of peace, unity, righteousness, and purpose. We are called to love all people and have relationships with people who don't know Jesus; however, it is healthy and wise to develop our closest relationships with people who have a healthy walk with the Lord.

2 Corinthians 6:14 says, "do not be yoked together with unbelievers. For what do righteousness and wickedness have in common? Or what fellowship can light have with darkness?" (NIV) This scripture isn't talking only about marriage for believers. It's referring to all relationships. It's so important that the people that you spend the most time with, are the most vulnerable with, open your life up to, allow to speak into your life, and are the most intimate with are believers that have a healthy growing relationship with God. The church is meant to be a place where you form those types of relationships with people.

1 Corinthians 15:33 reads, "bad company corrupts good character" (NIV) and it's true. Hanging around negative, gossipy, angry, selfish people or people who are living in sin will negatively affect your life. It's important to build relationships with people who are part of a local church

and are pursuing God in their personal lives because it's God's best to yoke ourselves with believers.

As I mentioned earlier, for years I tried to live God's best for my life outside a community of believers. It did not matter how much I read my Bible, how many sermons I listened to online, or how hard I tried to live right, I struggled to grow in God, maintain peace, and stay in a spiritually healthy place. But the moment I chose to give myself to a church, be committed to going, and integrate my life there, things started to change.

Now, I know full well that people in church aren't perfect. I have certainly come across people in church who have worldly symptoms of negativity, anger, gossip, and many other poor attitudes (myself included). The difference is, we are a family in Christ. We are brothers and sisters. It's important we learn how to get along with each other. If you give yourself to a church family, it will be the difficult people in your church who will rub off your rough edges and form Christ in you.

If a flower that was planted in the soil got up and moved every single time a thunderstorm came, it would never grow and blossom. Similarly, we cannot get up and change churches every single time someone offends us, does something we don't like, or rubs us the wrong way. We don't do that in our earthly families. We can't simply decide to get a new mom or brother if they upset us. We must learn to get along regardless.

In fact, I have learned through experience that when someone in the church gets under my skin, it's God trying to grow me up. While I've spent so many hours praying for God to change them, God has said to me, "No! You change and learn to love them."

I become stronger and healthier when I choose to grow in love, grace, and patience rather than complain about the people who upset or annoy me.

We must learn to stay planted in a church, so God can use us to polish the rough edges off each other! It's no good staying hurt, being offended, or harboring unforgiveness towards one another. In fact, those three things are probably some of the most detrimental attitudes a person can carry.

Do yourself a favor, and forgive people. Forgive those who hurt you, offend you, or mistreat you. It certainly is not easy but it's far harder and a lot more messy to stay hurt and offended. God wants you to be free.

While we are called to love non-believers and love those within our church, it's still important that we choose our friends and who we allow to speak into our lives. There will only be a few people you can be completely vulnerable with. It's important that you choose wisely the people who you decide to fully open your life up to. No one is perfect and all friendships and relationships take work at times. But your inner circle of close friends should be those who encourage you, pray with you, and build you up. They are going to keep you in a healthy place within yourself. Many people would do themselves a lot of good if they stopped spending much of their time around negative, jealous, and insecure people all the time.

FEED YOUR SPIRIT

Being planted in a local church body is essential to healthy living because you are able to be spiritually fed. Most people think healthy living includes two things: diet and exercise. What we put in our bodies and what we do with them is hugely important; however, equally important to this is what we put into our minds and hearts.

Not too long ago, I was sitting down watching TV with my husband. It was one of those shows where you are on the edge of your seat in suspense the whole time. When it was time for me to go to bed, I admittedly ran into the bed, pulled the sheets over myself, and sat there thinking about this show I just watched. Any strange noise I heard in the house caused me to jump a little bit. As I sat there with the sheets pulled up to my neck and my body on edge, I suddenly had the thought, "Why am I watching this and actually putting fear into my life?" I suddenly realized how it was silly for me to open myself up to something that would cause me to feel fear instead of faith.

What we allow ourselves to listen to is extremely important. When we, as believers, come together on a Sunday, we come together to hear the word of God. Romans 10:17 says, "Consequently, faith comes from hearing the message, and the message is heard through the word about Christ." (NIV)

If faith comes by hearing, how important is it that we put ourselves in a place to hear the word of God so we can live our lives in faith? Too many people struggle with anxiety, depression, and worry because they don't plant themselves in a church to hear the word preached. We must fill our lives with the word of God in our own devotional time and by hearing the preached word.

In the past seven years of being planted in a local church, I can count on one hand how many times I've missed church. I don't say that to boast about my church attendance track record. I say that because I know that

I need to go: I need to be around people of faith, I need to be encouraged by hearing testimonies of what God is doing in everyone's life, and I need to hear the preached word because it causes faith to grow inside me. I learn how to live the life God has for me. It's wonderful! The church is a gift from God that causes us to flourish if we choose to plant ourselves there. It's a fantastic blessing!

When we are in a place where faith is being preached, testimonies of God's goodness are being shared, and truth is being taught, we think more clearly, worry less, and see God's word work in our lives. What we listen to and meditate on greatly affects how we think. It's essential that we choose to listen to and meditate on the word of God. Proverbs 4:22 says this about the word of God, "for they are life to those who find them and health to one's whole body." (NIV)

The Bible is full of life giving words. It tells us not to worry (Matthew 6:25-34), that God will provide for us (Philippians 4:19), that God has good plans for us (Jeremiah 29:11),and that God loves us (John 3:16). It is jam-packed with promise!

When we meditate on negative things, we think negatively, which makes us worried, stressed out, confused, and upset. These attitudes are not healthy to have. However, Philippians 4:8 says, "Finally, brothers and sisters, whatever is true, whatever is noble, whatever is right, whatever is pure, whatever is lovely, whatever is admirable—if anything is excellent or praiseworthy—think about such things." (NLT)

When we meditate on these things, we flourish in ourselves. Many times, I have recalled something I heard on a Sunday, something I read in the Bible throughout the week, or a testimony someone shared with me, and doing this has brought me through a difficult time. Whether it was a difficult circumstance or trying to overcome a battle in my own mind, the Word of God brought me through. It is an essential ingredient in living a healthy, full life.

In the same way we are intentional about what foods we put in our bodies, we must be intentional about what we allow to go into our minds and hearts. Going to church on a regular and consistent basis means you are intentionally putting good spiritual food into your diet! It is not a chore, a drag, or a hardship. It is a blessing and gift from God for us as believers. Hebrews 10:24-25 encourages us to "And let us consider how we may spur one another on toward love and good deeds, not giving up meeting together, as some are in the habit of doing, but encouraging one another—and all the more as you see the Day approaching." (NIV)

The writer of Hebrews tells us not to forsake assembling together as some are in the habit of doing. It can be easy to get in the habit of missing church. However, I greatly encourage you to make it a part of your life and plant yourself in a body of believers. Give yourself to what God is doing in a local church. It's a place where you can express your spiritual gifts, grow in what God has called you to, and be encouraged from hearing testimonies from believers and hearing the word preached. It keeps us accountable to each other. The devil will try to do everything he can to keep you from going: the kids become naughty before you leave, you get into a spat with your spouse that morning, or you receive an invitation to go away for the weekend. While it's okay to go on vacation and take time away, it's important not to make a habit out it and forsake gathering together. Let go of offenses in your heart, forgive whoever you need to, and get planted in a good church, so you can flourish and live out everything your heavenly Father has for you!

APPLICATION POINT:

Pray and ask God about the relationships you have in your life right now. Who are you spending the most time with? Are they people who inspire you, build you up and bring you closer to God? 1 Corinthians 15:33 says that bad company corrupts good character, so it's important that you surround yourself with positive godly relationships. Be open to hearing God telling about who to spend more time with and who to distance yourself from.

Apple, Bacon & Dried Cranberry Salad

INGREDIENTS:

Handful kale

Handful Rocket

Handful Water Cress

1/2 cup quinoa

1 cube vegetable stock

1-2 Granny Smith Apples, sliced

5 Strips of bacon, cooked & chopped

1/2 cup dried cranberries

1/2 cup red onion, chopped

1/4 cup pumpkin seeds

Balsamic Glaze

Crumbled feta cheese to your liking

DIRECTIONS:

Boil 1 cup of water in a pot. Once the water is boiling, add the vegetable stock and quinoa. Cover and bring to

cont'd ▶

cont'd

a simmer. Allow the quinoa to cook for 10 -12 minutes. Wash greens. Place them in a bowl. Add the quinoa to the greens. Add all the ingredients together in a bowl. Drizzle the balsamic glaze on top, add the cheese.

CHAPTER 7

indulge in something yummy

P ray and ask God what foods and health habits
you should live by. Rather than try diet fad after
diet fad, ask your heavenly Father, the one who
created you and knows your inmost being (Psalm 139)
what healthy lifestyle is right for you.

God has something to say about our diet. God even had
something to say about the food Adam and Eve ate in
the garden. God said to Adam in Genesis 2:16-17, "You
may surely eat of every tree of the garden, but of the tree
of the knowledge of good and evil you shall not eat, for
in that day you eat of it you shall surely die." (ESV) Now,
I understand eating a piece of chocolate cake is not

going to alter the entire cosmic course of all humanity in heaven and earth, but I want to make the point that God knows his children. He has something to say about what foods will benefit us and what foods can harm us.

The most basic fundamental truth about a healthy diet is that every person should make a goal to eat a more plant based diet consisting of more vegetables and greens and some fruits, nuts, seeds, and fish.

1 Corinthians 6:12 says, "'All things are lawful for me,' but not all things are helpful. 'All things are lawful for me,' but I will not be dominated by anything." (ESV) We are free to do what we choose, but not everything is beneficial for us. When something begins to enslave you (cravings, food addictions, alcohol, etc.), it becomes a stronghold on your life and can sometimes be an idol. Jesus died on the cross for us to live free from any strongholds in our lives!

You are created uniquely and should eat uniquely. Diets don't work because what may cause someone else to gain weight may be what gives you essential energy. It's good to talk to your doctor about your health, eat a balanced diet, and research health. But asking God, the one who created you, will give you peace and insight into your life that no one else can. This is why praying and asking God when you should eat, how much you should eat, what foods you should eat, and with whom you should eat is so important. God wants you healthy, happy, and full of gusto for life to do the things he's calling you to do!

FUNDAMENTALS OF A HEALTHY DIET

Most of the food we eat today is completely different from the food our ancestors ate in the Bible. Today, much of our food comes from a factory that was created by man. Technology is amazing, but the God who created us and loves us and who put our organs, cells, and being together also provided food on the planet to nourish, bless, and generate healing to our bodies.

Healing and health is located in the foods God gives us

to eat. Our bodies are not sustained by Cheetos, white bread (pasta, rice, bagels), processed lunch meat, donuts, chips, candy, hormone injected meat, sugary beverages, and greasy fast food. The food created for our bodies comes straight from the earth. Fruit that grows on trees, vegetables that grow in the ground, nuts, seeds, whole grains, and legumes all come from the earth. Each one of these offers different valuable nutritional values that our bodies were created to need.

If we could combine the medicine and medical technology of today with the diet and movement people had in their lifestyle from early biblical times, we would be living a lot longer, we would have a better quality of life, diseases would be minimal, and sickness would be rare. God has given us so many brilliant doctors and intelligent scientists to formulate healing medicines and gifted health practices. And he has given us food that comes from the earth to allow us to live in the best health in the history of humanity! However, it is our turn to begin to take responsibility for our part.

Here are nine ingredients of a healthy lifestyle. Work on them one at a time, and take it slowly:

1. Begin to cook at home more. You will eat less with small portions, and the food won't be loaded with salt and butter.

2. Drink more water instead of juice, pop, coffee, or alcohol.

3. Increase your vegetable intake. Try to eat a variety of colored food at every meal (i.e. red peppers, purple egg plant, green kale, orange carrots, blue blueberries, yellow lemons).

4. Eliminate processed foods as much as you can from your diet (i.e. fast food, chips, white grains, candy).

5. Incorporate movement into your life (i.e. gardening, biking, running, dancing, sports, walking, kayaking).

6. Practice the fruit of the Spirit: love, joy, peace, patience, kindness, goodness, faithfulness, gentleness, and self-control. Also, a healthy dose of forgiveness is highly important to your health as well.

7. Take care of yourself by relaxing, having fun regularly, and being with friends and family.

8. Maintain positive relationships in your life. If there are toxic relationships, pray and ask God for wisdom on how you should manage them.

9. Develop a close and intimate relationship with God by reading the Bible, praying, and fellowshipping with him.

DECONSTRUCT YOUR CRAVINGS

So many of us unknowingly eat whatever we feel like and don't take the time to ask ourselves or ask God why we're doing it. We simply get frustrated with our cravings, blame ourselves for a lack of self-control, and binge diet. We can, though, learn to understand these cravings. For me, I knew I craved sweets, but I never stopped to notice when or why I craved them.

Once I began to pay attention to my cravings, I noticed I craved sweets when I was around friends or family.

After praying about it, God showed me that food was an avenue to bond with my friends and family. Growing up, I would always go get ice cream with my step-dad or bake homemade cookies with my mom. My best friend and I indulged in anything chocolate when we wanted to either relax, have a heart-to-heart, or comfort ourselves after a long day. I discovered that my hang up wasn't a lack of self control, it was a subconscious fear that if I gave up sweet treats when I was together with friends or family, I would be lose out on bonding with them in a way. As silly as that might sound to you, that was one of the ways I began to deconstruct my own cravings. After I had realized that connection, I began to slowly create new ways to bond with my friends and family that didn't relate to food. I was surprised to find that most of the time, they didn't mind if I turned down a sugary snack. It was just all in my head.

I don't believe I ever would have been able to navigate past my sugar cravings if I had not discovered what I was truly craving: deep meaningful relationships in my life.

Everyone's cravings are usually rooted in different fears, hang-ups, or issues. Sometimes issues of insecurity developed from childhood resulting in emotional eating to comfort a past hurt they've experienced. Sometimes, it's issues of not having enough fun in life, so junk food is used to make moments more enjoyable and fun. Sometimes issues of a lack of love from earthly parents can cause someone to gorge on food to satisfy that gap in their heart. Other times, there is no issue there at all but a lack of simple food education.

Health is about more than doing 50 sit-ups a day. It is about understanding yourself and how your own body operates. If you can understand something, you are more likely to have power over it. It's when we don't understand something that it has power over us. Dieting will give you a list of foods to eat and not eat. You will always struggle to stick to the diet, stay on the diet, and control your cravings. It will never allow you to go to the root of the problem to bring enlightenment about yourself. Listening to your body, paying attention to your food patterns, and being educated on food will cause understanding and knowledge that will empower you to make wise decisions. You will begin to choose the right foods because you will desire to feed your body foods that make it feel good. Take a few minutes to pray and answer these questions:

What foods do you crave and why do you crave them?

What would you be losing out on if you were to give up that food?

When do you usually crave those foods?

How is that food serving you or not serving you?

Who first introduced that food into your life and why?

How do you feel after eating that food?

HEALTH IS A JOURNEY NOT AN OVERNIGHT DIET PILL

We are all on a health continuum. By making small changes each day, we will move forward in our own health journey to becoming healthier and healthier. But you must start where you are.

There will always be a healthier option for us. Healthy is relative based on where you are on your health continuum.

No one can go from eating fast food every day to eating a clean plant-based diet overnight. It's unrealistic for change to happen that drastically and be sustainable. However, if you transition from fast food every day to fast food three times a week and then to eating food at home, you can see progressive and lasting change. You can begin eating healthy home-cooked food like sautéed vegetables, small amounts of meat with lots of greens, fruits, and some whole grains.

Give yourself permission to make gradual changes. It frees you from feeling guilty for not going from McDonalds to eating kale over night. Being healthier is going to be different for everyone depending on where you are at in your health journey.

My husband is certainly not into healthy eating like I am. When we first got married his diet consisted of chips and queso, pancakes with ketchup on them, meat lovers pizza, and candy. I realized the more and more I tried to hound him for cleaning up his diet, the worse it got.

One night, he suggested pizza for dinner. Before I could even say no, he said, "We will order a pepperoni pizza but make it a healthy pizza and add green pepper on top." I knew in his head, he actually thought that was healthy. Instead of laughing in his face for thinking that by simply adding green pepper to a pepperoni pizza was healthy, I said, "I'm so proud of you for making a healthier choice! Let's do it!"

By encouraging small changes over a long period of time, healthy, long-lasting transformation begins to occur instead of yo-yo binge dieting, which actually causes more weight-gain in the end.

THE POWER OF CROWDING OUT

I learned a fantastic food tactic at nutrition school: crowding out. Crowd out your bad food with good food. Simply increase your intake of vegetables, greens, fish, fruits, nuts and legumes to naturally minimize the junk food. Celebrate what you can say yes to. Whatever we tell ourselves we can't have usually becomes the thing we start to desire. It's better to get excited about introducing new healthy options that you might not have ever explored before.

Your taste buds can change, believe it or not. By slowly and steadily adding more greens to your diet (even if it's a dark green salad and French fries), your body naturally begins to crave what it was meant to thrive on the first place. You will begin to enjoy the boost of energy you feel, the improved sleep, skin, and figure! The pros will eventually outweigh the cons, and you will be well on your way to a more natural and healthy diet.

I always hear people don't enjoy healthy eating because they don't get full on a carrot stick or small garden salad. I don't either. I was never interested in eating healthy food because it didn't have much flavor to me. I thought you could only eat salads to get vegetables in your diet. I didn't want to only eat boring, unsatisfying salads. I wanted a burger!

I started to experiment with my food. Instead of just having iceberg lettuce with tomatoes, cucumber, and onion, I started to try new things. I discovered having copious amounts of vegetables in my salad helped me to feel fuller longer. I learned the darker the leaf, the more nutritious. I started to buy dark collard greens, kale, and spinach. I would use those greens in my salad and add a lot of different kinds of vegetables to it. I started to add legumes and beans to them as well. I would add quinoa, wheat berries, or couscous. I gradually stopped dumping massive amounts of salad dressing on my salad and began to add some oil and lemon or nothing at all sometimes because the vegetable flavors were enough!

Adding in a big variety of vegetables, dark greens, some fruits, legumes, seeds, beans, and grains into my salads made me feel full on healthy foods. Not to mention, I really enjoyed the variety. I started to not skimp on any of my meals because feeling full wasn't an unhealthy thing if I was full on the right foods.

I also began to understand that fat was not a cursed food. In fact, many items in the store that say "Low-Fat" are usually replaced with greater amounts of sugar. It's not fat that makes you fat, but it's sugar that is the enemy. Stick to full fat foods. Incorporating foods that contain good fats caused me to feel fuller longer. Foods like nuts, avocados, nut butters, or coconut oil helped me to not feel hungry and were good for me.

THE MEAT AND DAIRY DILEMMA

I am not against meat. However, in the Western world, we should lessen our consumption of it. Truthfully, the star food item on our plate should be the vegetables, not the meat. The side dishes should consist of a meat, grain, or fruit.

Many people feel that meat is a must have in their diet because they believe they will starve to death without some protein. Fortunately, there are several other options that contain protein that aren't animal products. Foods like beans, quinoa, chia seeds, nuts, yogurt, eggs, and kale are all fantastic alternative protein sources. While animal meat is not a bad food, eating a more plant-based diet is a healthier option. We should really limit ourselves to eating only a fist-sized portion of meat a maximum of 2-3 times per week! By doing this, we can minimize the spread of disease, sickness, and infection by being on a more plant based diet. It's also more sustainable and environmentally friendly.

If you are going to buy meat, it is worth the extra cash to buy it organic. Meat is not unhealthy. It only becomes questionable when it's consumed excessively or is packed with hormones and additives. Most of the meat sold in grocery stores has been injected with many different hormones. And the animals that were used were raised in very poor living conditions, causing the animal to be sickly. Be sure to look for labels that say

"Free-Range," "Organic," or "No Hormones" on them.

Dairy is not right for everyone. If you struggle with frequent coughing, mucus, asthma, stomach aches, skin rashes or digestion issues you may want to consider eliminating dairy from your diet for two weeks to see if your symptoms improve. You will not be able to have even a trace amount of dairy in your diet throughout this two-week period or the food test will not work. This can be done with gluten and citrus foods as well, which are also known to cause similar bodily reactions.

If you like milk, you might want to switch to a nut milk. There are many varieties that can be found at your local grocery store. Be careful to read the labels, though, because they can sometimes have added sugar in them. Making your own nut milk at home can be an easy alternative. Finding a homemade nut milk recipe on the internet is very simple.

Yogurt is another very popular "healthy" food people pick out in the store. Many times though, the yogurt is loaded with copious amounts of sugar. So, look for plain Greek yogurt. You can add more flavor to the yogurt by adding in your favorite fruit and some honey or pure maple syrup on top. I like a bit of crunch in mine, so I'll add granola or nuts as well. It's important to read the labels because granola can be packed with sugar many times as well.

HEALTHY DOESN'T MEAN BORING

There are so many ways you can add variety to your food by cooking them differently. I am a strong believer that if you don't like a certain vegetable (or vegetables in general), it's probably because you haven't had it prepared properly or seasoned well!

Here are a few ways you can prepare your vegetables: *boil, bake, stir-fry, steam. sauté, roast, blanch, stew, grill.*

Add a little salt and black pepper or cayenne with chili flakes, and maybe some olive oil or lemon, and your vegetables suddenly come alive in your mouth.

Mix it up and eat seasonally. In God's wisdom, as the

seasons change, so do the foods. Our bodies require something different to help us thrive in the season we find ourselves.

In the summer, salads are everywhere! They are a refreshing food option because they help cool our bodies down during the warm summer months.

In the summer, we don't mind eating raw fruits and vegetables because our bodies want to stay cool. Most people struggle to do a detox or raw food diet in the winter because it's unnatural for our bodies. During this season we are trying to conserve our body's natural heat. In the winter, we crave fattier and heavier foods to warm ourselves up. Foods like cucumbers, peppers, asparagus, zucchini or eggplant all taste better in the spring and summer because we naturally crave lighter foods then.

In winter, most of us tend to gain 3-5lbs because our bodies are preparing themselves for the cold months. I still enjoy salads during colder weather because I warm up my vegetables before I put them on my greens. Make a big bed of kale (or a favorite dark green of your choice) and sauté vegetables on the stove or roast them in the oven. Then you can add them to your salad instead of having them raw; it warms our bodies up! I usually add more beans and grains to my salads in the winter because our bodies crave heavier foods.

Soup is also something we crave in the winter because it keeps us warm! It's hard to mess up a soup recipe, and you can make large batches at once to have later in the week. We also tend to crave more meat and fat in the winter as a means of conserving and storing more energy. Eating small amounts of animal meat and healthy fats are a good option for winter time meals.

Root vegetables are a more common vegetable in the cold months because they grow underground and withstand the harsh winters. Having a pepper in the winter isn't going to taste as good as eating it in the summer because they aren't in season, and they loose their flavor. However, broccoli, chard, parsnips, squash, onions, carrots, and leeks are great winter vegetables to enjoy! By learning what foods are in season at what time will be better on your wallets and taste buds because the food in season is more likely to be on sale and taste much better!

It's more natural to cook in harmony with the seasons. God knew what foods our bodies would need to give us the best energy and cognitive abilities during certain seasons.

PRACTICAL TIPS AND TRICKS

1. Double up on a recipe. Eat some now and freeze the rest of it for later in the week or month. This cuts down on kitchen time and enables you to still have home-cooked meals in a flash during busy week nights.

2. Using precooked rice, oats, quinoa, or other grains allows you to use them in a variety of ways: side dishes with spices and herbs, salad toppings, or for breakfast with berries and natural sweeteners.

3. Try to eat foods with five ingredients or less on the label. Better yet, the ones that don't have a label, like an apple.

4. If you're reading the ingredient list (by the way, always read the ingredient list), and you cannot pronounce the ingredients, chances are, they won't make sense to your body either. Don't buy it.

5. Purchase the majority of your food from the produce section. Shop around the outside of the store and steer clear from the center aisles if you can. Normally, all the factory made food is there.

6. Be sure to buy organic meat and to steer clear from added hormones and additives that are very unhealthy for your body. It's worth the extra few bucks!

7. Switch from white grains to whole grains. Ezekiel bread is a real whole grain bread. If you can smash the bread so it's flat, it is not a whole grain. Labels can be confusing so make sure there are few ingredients that are pronounceable. Also, you can purchase quinoa,

buckwheat, oats, or brown rice to have on hand in your kitchen. You can use them in a morning porridge, a grain for a dinner dish, or for making whole grain flour.

8. Try shopping at a local farmers market to ensure your produce is organic. It's also environmentally friendly for our planet to go through local farmers, and you also support local business.

9. You can find the foods that are sprayed with the most pesticides each season from The Dirty Dozen List. It's a list online that will show you which foods you should splurge the extra few dollars to buy organic.

10. Spice things up! I usually have basil, paprika, cumin, coriander, turmeric, curry powder, cayenne, chili flakes, mint, oregano, and cinnamon at all times in my cupboard. I also have lemon and lime on hand. By adding different spices to your vegetables, grains or sometimes meats and fish can really change an entire dish. Healthy food doesn't have to be tasteless; use some spice!

11. I always keep a bag of frozen berries, peeled frozen bananas, and frozen greens in my freezer. I will take some of the berries out of the freezer, allow them to defrost, and add them to my yogurt or grain. I use frozen bananas and greens in smoothies a lot. Produce can go bad within a week, but there is no pressure to use it quickly when it's frozen. Save yourself some cash from throwing away produce.

APPLICATION POINT:

Take a moment to consider your diet. Are you feeding your body foods that will nourish it, protect it and give it energy? Make a food journal this week of the foods you eat. Notice how you feel after you eat them. Do they give you stomach cramps, indigestion, heart burn, bloating, sleepiness or gas? What mood were you in when you had that food? Were you happy, sad, bored or celebrating? Being aware of your own eating habits is the first step to making a lasting change.

Healthy Chocolate Ice Cream with Berries

INGREDIENTS:

1 frozen banana

1-2 Tbsp smooth organic peanut butter

1 Tbsp coco powder

1/4 cup brown rice milk

3 strawberries

DIRECTIONS:

In a blender combine all the ingredients. You might need to blend, stop, mix with a spoon, then blend again to get the ingredients to mix well. Cut up the strawberries and place on top. Add dark chocolate chips if you wish!

Gooey Chocolate Brownies

INGREDIENTS

1 15 ounce can of garbanzo beans (chickpeas), drained and rinsed

2 eggs

½ cup agave nectar

2 tsp vanilla extract

⅓ cup cocoa powder

½ tsp baking powder

pinch of salt

¼ cup semi-sweet chocolate chips

olive oil

Berries or banana to top!

DIRECTIONS

Preheat oven to 350 degrees. Wipe 8x8 in pan with olive oil to grease the pan.

Add all the ingredients except for the chocolate chips into a blender.

Blend all the ingredients until smooth.

Once all ingredients are well blended, fold in the chocolate chips with a spatula as you pour the mixture into the baking dish.

Bake for 25-30 minutes. Make sure the centre is cooked through!

Cool, slice, and serve. Add whatever fruit you like on top for added flavor.

CHAPTER 8

shake your booty

When I was growing up, every time I would hop out of the car to go into my dance class, my mom would yell out the car window as loud as she could, "Shake your booty!"

If I was feeling silly enough, right before I would step into the class, I would stick my butt out and do a little wiggle.

I was used to being at the dance studio four to five nights a week. I absolutely loved it! As I got older, I had to stop taking the classes because I moved away to college. The years following I really struggled to find any sort of exercise that I enjoyed, like I did with my dance classes.

Eventually, I studied Exercise Science in college, and I was amazed at how people in my classes enjoyed doing squats. They actually enjoyed push-ups, crunches, sprints, and the rest of it! I couldn't understand why anyone would want to do that sort of thing when they could sit on the couch and watch a movie instead.

I started to feel guilty for my sedentary lifestyle, and I tried to start running. I would run for a little while, but eventually I'd get bored and stop. I struggled for a long time trying to force myself to stick to an exercise regime. I would feel guilty for doing nothing and worry about gaining weight. Then at the same time, when I started to run, I never really enjoyed it and would eventually stop. I was never able to stick to maintaining a consistent exercise regime.

I can remember struggling with this issue for a few years, and I decided to get some help by meeting a health coach. I wasn't really sure what that was, but I discovered it was someone who helped people reach their personal health goals.

I told her my exercise dilemma. I explained that I absolutely hated going to the gym, running around a track, and doing push-ups. I could do it for a little while, but then I'd always eventually slip back into my sedentary ways. I hated exercise. So I asked her, "What should I do?"

"If you don't want to exercise, then don't." She answered.

I stood there confused.

"But, you're a health coach. Aren't you supposed to tell me to exercise? Isn't it unhealthy if we don't exercise? That if we don't get 30 minutes of aerobic exercise a day, it's bad for us?" I responded.

"Perhaps, but if you don't enjoy doing it, you're not going to do it."

I continued to stand there puzzled.

"So what do you enjoy?" She continued. "Do you enjoy gardening? Going for long walks with friends? Dancing to your favorite music in your kitchen?" She asked.

Now, those things I did enjoy.

She told me in the end if I didn't like to exercise, that finding enjoyable ways to just simply move my body was a way for me to get physical activity into my day.

DO WHAT YOU ENJOY

We think unless we are at the gym for an hour, pushing ourselves, sweating like a maniac, and doing squats, the workout is pointless. But in the end, we just do nothing and complain about it. I would say most of us struggle with this exercise dilemma. We either force ourselves to exercise and absolutely hate it so we stop or we simply just don't do it at all and beat ourselves up for it.

However, I've learned that if you can just start with something you enjoy, you will be more likely to do it for the rest of your life. Doing some form of movement consistently for the rest of your life is much better for you than a stop and start exercise routine mixed with frustration.

I'm sure you know what I'm talking about. Every January gyms get packed out with people and their New Years' "Get Fit" Resolutions. By March, many of those people have stopped. Why? Because people will never continue to do something long term when they don't enjoy it. The emotional effects of beating yourself up for a lack of self control is so discouraging, many people eventually just give up on the whole idea of exercise all together.

Starting with some form of movement you enjoy will help you stay consistent and possibly turn you on to other forms of exercise in the future. Doing something is better than nothing!

You see, because of that conversation I had with the health coach, I saw exercise in a new light. Since I had gone to school for Exercise Science and was surrounded by people who genuinely enjoyed hard core physical activity, I truly thought that I needed to become like them. I had no idea that I could explore movement and discover something that I enjoyed that was more like me. It seemed my whole mindset about what "exercise" had to look like shifted, and it opened up a whole new idea of personalized movement.

I had fresh motivation to discover a new fun hobby for myself. Instead of forcing myself to do something I didn't enjoy, I began to wonder what type of movement was out there for me that I really did enjoy.

UNDERSTAND THE ACTIVITY YOU ENJOY

Over time, I realized I really enjoyed long walks outside with my dog, friends, or alone with God. I looked forward to them. It was stress-relieving, calming, and enjoyable for me. I didn't know that walks counted as exercise if I wasn't sweaty and out of breath. Eventually, I reasoned with myself that going for a walk was much better than sitting on my couch.

I also discovered I really appreciated nature. Sometimes on my walk, I would begin to just chat to God. I would connect with him in a different way during those times than I would alone in my room. I loved that it opened up a new way for me to encounter him.

Finding activities in our lives that can impact physical, emotional, and spiritual health is highly motivating. We are emotional creatures. When we do something that brings stability, balance, peace, or joy to us, it is extremely beneficial for our health.

After realizing I enjoyed the outdoors and walking, I simply just started there. I would wake up in the morning and just go for a walk. I had to turn off the voices in my head that said, "This is a waste of time! If you're not sweating, it's not doing anything for you! Why don't you run!" I had been so sedentary for so long, I knew that I just needed to begin to create a space in my life for movement if I was going to make this lifestyle change.

As I started to walk a few mornings or afternoons during

the week, I found it to be a special time with God and with myself. If friends would want to meet up for a coffee, I'd suggest going for a walk with the coffee to go. I started to find ways to just add it into my life.

After I had incorporated walking in my lifestyle for a few months, I started to make it a bit more challenging. I would find hills to power walk up, I would intermittently run in between walking, or sometimes I would do walking lunges. I honestly started to enjoy moving my body. I found a greater level of energy, fewer mood-swings, and my body felt better. If I missed a morning, it wouldn't worry me because the genuine enjoyment of the movement would eventually call my name. and I'd get back to it.

I naturally started to become curious about other forms of movement that I might enjoy in addition to walking. I discovered an aerobic dance class at a local gym and checked it out. I had a blast! I loved the energy in the room, the movement, and how it made me feel.

I discovered I really disliked high intensity interval training. If you're not sure what that is, it's performing a series of intense aerobic exercise with short bouts of less intense exercise. This type of exercise is extremely good for muscular endurance, strength, and your aerobic activity, but it is very physically demanding. I decided I enjoyed this exercise once a week or every now and then, but it wouldn't pull me out of bed in the morning.

Once I stopped looking at exercise by how many calories I needed to burn, completing 10 more sit-ups from the time before, or wondering if I had worked out hard enough, and I started focusing on having fun, it completely changed my perspective.

MAKE YOUR OWN GOALS

Health is about self-discovery. We must learn to evaluate ourselves if we are going to be successful. Here are a few things to ask yourself:

• *What are your exercise goals?*

• *What are your movement priorities?*

• *What interests you about exercise and movement?*

• *What's your personality like?*

• *What season of life are you in?*

Finding answers to all of those components will help set you up for success in staying healthy.

For example, some people reading this might have a much more competitive edge than me. They might find that beating their last score or keeping track of their calorie count is motivating and helpful for them. They might greatly enjoy intense training and absolutely hate a large aerobic dance class. The point that I am making here is a successful, healthy lifestyle is rooted in self-discovery.

By beginning to listen to yourself, accept yourself, and understand yourself, you can find foods, movement, and healthy habits that suit you.

What are your goals? If you are looking to lose weight to

fit into an outfit for a special occasion, then doing a more intense exercise program to burn more calories will be necessary for you to meet your goal. If you're like me and you are looking to simply find a form of movement to help you gradually loose weight or maintain your weight and stay healthy over your entire lifetime, it's important to find a movement you simply enjoy. Evaluating what your goal is for this particular time will help direct you in the type of movement you need to meet that goal.

Are you introverted or extroverted? If you are an introverted competitive person, you might enjoy running every day by yourself and trying to beat your last score each time. If you are an extroverted person who just enjoys having fun, perhaps joining a group kickboxing class would motivate you. You might find the social aspect of a class to be more enjoyable than if you were alone.

What are your priorities? It's so important to consider what your priorities are. Is it more of a priority for it to be convenient or held accountable? If it's convenience, purchase a workout DVD to watch at home or keep weights in your house to exercise with. If it's accountability, join a group exercise program, hire a personal trainer, or go walking with a friend a few times a week.

Are you more competitive and results driven or are you looking for something that is stress-relieving and light-hearted. If you are a more results driven type person, you might find it highly motivating to sign up for a 5k run or a marathon. That goal will cause you to stay motivated to be consistent in your exercise plan. Or perhaps joining a community sports team, like volleyball or soccer, would be beneficial as you might enjoy there being a winner and a loser. If you find you're more interested in finding something that will target your emotive side, look into a yoga, pilates, or dance classes. You'll need to be careful with some yoga classes as they can become deeply spiritual in the wrong stuff. Finding a class that focuses on purely the movement is best.

By knowing yourself and evaluating your schedule, interests, priorities, and goals, you can discover what healthy habits work best for you personally.

EXERCISE VS. MOVEMENT

Most of us know and realize that exercise is good for us. We understand it helps our bodies function better, keeps us strong mentally and physically, helps us to have more energy among many other benefits. What most of us struggle with is actually doing it.

For some reason, the thought of going to the gym, running on a track, lifting weights, and getting sweaty just didn't sound appealing to me. Whatever movement you enjoy doing, do it and find life in it.

When I began to change my mindset from an "exercise" mentality to a "movement" mentality, I started to embrace doing some sort of physical activity in my daily life.

What does that look like for you?

Instead of leaving the yard work to my husband, I started to mow my own lawn; that's a workout! I would work in my yard, dig holes, pull weeds, turn over dirt, and plant flowers. By the end of it, I would be a sweaty mess. I found it was something I could do, because not only did I get a work-out, but my yard looked pretty after.

I cleaned my own house: vacuuming, cleaning the floors on my hands and knees, and scrubbing the bathtub. Those were all things I needed to get done anyway, and I would put my favorite music on to make it fun. This would get my heart rate up by doing that.

I found dead space in my day, and I began to work my muscles out then. When I would brush my teeth, instead of just standing there, I would do squats in front of the mirror. Before I would put the milk away in the fridge, I would lift the jug above my head 10 times and work my shoulders. When I was standing at the stove, I would do calf raises as I was stirring the food in the pot. I simply began to notice this dead space throughout my day, and I'd find little ways to keep myself active.

On my journey of adding more movement into my life, I hit a wall once winter came. Where I am from, we get a lot of snow, and it's extremely cold. I always complained about the snow because it kept me cooped up inside. It was seriously cramping my movement routine.

One day, I splurged and bought myself some top quality waterproof winter snow boots. I put them on with a warm winter coat, hat, scarf, and gloves and went for a walk outside in the middle of winter. I realized that when you dress appropriately for the weather, you can move in almost all types of outside conditions. My feet were no longer wet and cold, my body stayed warm, and I started to enjoy the beautiful white winter wonderland around me. You don't need to have perfect weather conditions to get out and move around, just have fitting apparel!

As women, we are called to be strong in our spirit, mind, and body. God is interested in us thriving in all three. It is a myth that women should not weight train because they will bulk up and look manly. However, it is one of the best things we can do for ourselves. Women who lift weights are less likely to have osteoporosis when they get older, and they can reduce their risk of injuries, back pain, arthritis, diabetes, heart disease, and depression. When we lift weights, our muscles become more lean, which then increases our resting metabolism and burns fat. Lifting weights can make us feel more confident navigating through life physically like when we are carrying in a large load of groceries, picking our children up, moving furniture around, or lifting things in general.

STEWARD YOUR BODY SO YOU HAVE LONGEVITY IN GOD

God has a purpose and a calling for all of our lives. I want to steward the body God has blessed me with so I can run the race he has called me to with endurance and strength until the day I die. It is truly a shame to think that many people forfeit years of their life in serving God because they didn't steward their health well. I want to still be able to do all the things God is calling me to, even in my old age because I've stewarded my health.

If we are called to do the things that Jesus did, we

must live the way Jesus lived. In a very practical sense, Jesus walked everywhere he went. While I'm very aware they did not have cars back then, I do believe that God gave us muscles, joints, and ligaments so that they could be used. By simply starting where you are and taking one small step forward, you can begin to see transformation in your life.

For a long time, I wasn't interested in exercise. One day, I started with where I was and God has helped me to go to new levels in my health and daily movement. You do not need to begin by running a mile and doing 20 push-ups if that is not where you are. Ask yourself what is one small step you can take today that can help you to move forward into tomorrow?

Don't allow yourself to be overwhelmed by the number you see on your scale so that you already feel defeated. You must simply accept where you are, evaluate your lifestyle, and take one small step forward in whatever that looks like for you. I promise if you can honor each stage of your health journey and celebrate each big or small achievement, it will motivate you to keep going!

"I can do all things through him who strengthens me."
(Philippians 4:13, ESV)

APPLICATION POINT:

What movement do you enjoy? What motivates you? What is something small you can start doing today to help incorporate movement into your every day life? It could be as small as choosing to park far away each time you go to the store or as big as signing up for a marathon. Begin to formulate a measurable and realistic plan to add movement into your life. Remember this is a life-long journey, not a sprint so starting slow is okay! Make sure to celebrate yourself along the way!

MELISSA HUGHES

SHE CAN LAUGH

salvation prayer

One of the most important decisions you could ever make about your health is choosing to make Jesus the Lord of your life. The Bible says this about Jesus in Isaiah 53:5

"But he was pierced for our rebellion, crushed for our sins. He was beaten so we could be whole. He was whipped so we could be healed." (NLT)

None of us are perfect. The Bible says that all of us have fallen short of God's standard of perfection (Romans 3:23) because of sin. Sin separates us from God because he is completely sin free; he is Holy. The Bible says that the consequence for sin is death and eternal separation from God. Hang on though; I have good news for you... Not only is God holy, he is also completely full of love.

Because God saw this separation between us and so loved you and I, he chose to send his only son, Jesus Christ, to take the penalty for our sin upon himself and die on the cross (John 3:16). Three days later, Jesus rose from the grave and is now seated in heaven with God (1 Corinthians 15:4).

The Bible says that whoever believes that Jesus died on the cross for their sins and rose again, and confesses with their mouths that he's Lord shall receive eternal salvation (Romans 10:9).

Jesus loves you so much and died for you because he wants a personal relationship with you. He wants to give you a brand new heart and a fresh start today. Your heavenly Father created you for a great purpose and has a wonderful plan for your life. If you would like to meet Jesus today for the first time and have your sins forgiven and receive a brand new heart in Christ, you can pray this prayer out loud to God now:

"Lord Jesus, I recognize I have sinned and fallen short of your standard of perfection. I ask you to forgive me of all my sins

right now. I confess that you are Lord and I invite you to come into my heart and be the Lord of my life. I am saved, I'm clean, I'm set free, I'm healed and I believe you have a good plan for my life. Amen."

Wow! Take a moment and relish in the fact you've now come into a personal love relationship with Jesus! It's important that you phone a Christian you know and tell them about the decision you've made. I want to encourage you to get yourself a Bible and begin reading it (Matthew is a good book to start in). It's also important to surround yourself with other Christians by joining a church and getting baptized in water and in the Holy Spirit!

You have a fantastic future ahead of you! I'd love to hear from you if you've met Jesus today! You can email me at *melissa@thepointchurch.com* and share with me your experience!

God Bless You!

ABOUT THE AUTHOR

Born and raised in the United States, Melissa Hughes now lives in Wales with her Welsh husband Keane Hughes and they are expecting their first child, Ella Lilly Nia Hughes. Melissa has a Bachelors of Science from Grand Valley State University in Exercise Science along with a Holistic Health Coach certification from the Institute for Integrative Nutrition. Previous to moving to the UK, Melissa ran her own business called, Indulge Health Coaching where she coached many women on the principals used in this book. Her husband and her now lead The Point Church South Wales in Aberdare, one of several church campuses through The Point church network. One of her biggest passions is to help women everywhere live sustainable healthy lives through biblical principals. She is an avid dog-lover, people-befriender, and faith-sharer.

Other titles from

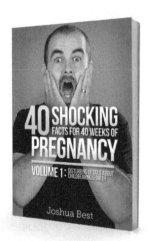

40 Shocking Facts for 40 Weeks of
Pregnancy - Volume 1: Disturbing
Details about Childbearing & Birth

Available at most book retailers.
$9.95 Paperback
$2.99 eBook

40 Shocking Facts for 40 Weeks of
Pregnancy - Volume 2: Terrifying
Truths about Babies & Breastfeeding

Available at most book retailers.
$9.95 Paperback
$2.99 eBook

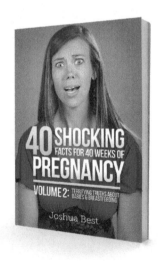

Visit unprecedentedpress.com for more information.

Made in the USA
Las Vegas, NV
23 December 2022

64014747R00115